This is What America Looks Like

This is What America Looks Like

Washington Writers' Publishing House Anthology
Poetry & Fiction from DC, Maryland, Virginia

Kathleen Wheaton, Publisher
Caroline Bock and Jona Colson, Editors

Jona Colson

Washington Writers' Publishing House
Washington, DC

COVER ART by Dana Ellyn and Matt Sesow
COVER DESIGN by Lou Ann Robinson
ORIGINAL INTERIOR ART by Mark Blech
BOOK DESIGN and TYPESETTING by Barbara Shaw
PROOFREADING by Kristin Scearce

Library of Congress Cataloging-in-Publication Data

Names: Bock, Caroline, editor. | Colson, Jona, 1979- editor.
Title: This is what America looks like : the Washington Writers' Publishing House anthology ; poetry & fiction from DC, Maryland, Virginia / Caroline Bock and Jona Colson, editors.
Description: Washington, D.C. : Washington Writers' Publishing House, [2021] | Summary: "This Is What America Looks Like - 100 poets and fiction writers from DC, Maryland and Virginia on the creative state of our nation"— Provided by publisher.
Identifiers: LCCN 2020051359 | ISBN 9781941551257 (paperback) | ISBN 9781941551264 (ebook)
Subjects: LCSH: American poetry—21st century. | Short stories, American.
Classification: LCC PS536.3 .T53 2021 | DDC 810.8/006—dc23
LC record available at https://lccn.loc.gov/2020051359

Printed in the United States of America

WASHINGTON WRITERS' PUBLISHING HOUSE
2814 5th Street, NE, #1301
Washington, D.C. 20017
More information: www.washingtonwriters.org

CONTENTS

"I hear America singing…" —WALT WHITMAN

"I, too, sing America." —LANGSTON HUGHES

A Short History of a Small Press

"EVERYTHING STARTS with a thought," Maryland Poet Laureate Grace Cavalieri once wrote. "Chairs, babies, poems, and institutions."

The thought that became Washington Writers' Publishing House first materialized in 1975, when four D.C. poets—Grace, John McNally, Deirdra Baldwin, and Terrence Winch—frustrated by the dearth of local publishing outlets, decided to start their own damn poetry press. Each group of poets published would then work on behalf of publishing other poets, creating an eventual pyramid of poets. Authors would cover half the printing costs; the press would be a cooperative. It was the Seventies, after all—it would be beautiful.

Somehow, this little scheme got a National Endowment for the Arts grant. And the four founders, two of whom called themselves hippies in their author bios, devised a book distribution method they called "Drop-and-Split," whereby Grace would run into bookstores, sneak new WWPH volumes onto shelves, and then dash away into Deirdra's waiting getaway car. It turned out that the books sold—or at least left the stores—though the press got no money for them. "But," Grace said, "the poetry was on the street."

Anyway, WWPH got noticed. Nationally known poets—E. Ethelbert Miller, Kim Roberts, Jehanne Dubrow—published early books here. And little by little, the press evolved from outlaw to institution. Authors were no longer asked to help pay for printing; the blind-judged annual contest offered cash prizes. Winners signed contracts obliging them to work for the press for two years following publication. Some authors split at the stroke of midnight two years later; others have stayed on for decades.

In 2000, WWPH began publishing fiction—short story collections and novels—as well as poetry. Readings are held at storied Washington bookstores; customers pay cover price plus tax at the register.

This isn't to say that WWPH "makes money" in any commonly understood sense of the phrase. Forty-six years after its founding, the staff is still all volunteer; the budget is the slenderest of shoestrings. Putting out two books a year is an annual miracle.

And since behind every miracle are miracle workers, two must be named here: Barbara Shaw, who has typeset every WWPH title since the inception, making each book specifically lovely; and Jean Feldman, our angel benefactor, for whom the Poetry Prize is named.

In 1995, WWPH published a poetry anthology, *Hungry As We Are*, referencing not only the trope of the starving artist but the poetic appetite for life. That book celebrated twenty years of the press, an unimaginable anniversary in the days of Drop-and-Split. Among its 210 poems are two by former Minnesota Senator Eugene McCarthy, who failed to win the 1968 Democratic Presidential nomination.

However, we admit to breathing a sigh of relief when no Democratic candidate for the 2020 Presidential contest answered our call for submissions to the anthology you now hold in your hands. It would have been a dispiriting omen.

The impulse behind this collection hasn't been so much celebration as—let's be honest—rage. The chant *"This is what America looks like"*—in all its racial, ethnic, gender, age and ability-diverse fury—which echoed down the January 2017 Women's March, rattled through the brain of [2018 Fiction Prize winner] Caroline Bock, until she persuaded the press that it was high time we published another anthology. This iteration would have poetry *and* short fiction; the chant would be its writing prompt as well as its title. We agreed to suspend manuscript contests for a year to conserve funds and editorial stamina. Jona Colson, who won the 2018 Jean Feldman Poetry Prize, joined Caroline as co-editor, and off they went.

Between the thought that sparked the anthology and the chosen submission dates came a deadly pandemic and the sickening police execution of a Black grocery customer named George Floyd, both disasters sparking a national reckoning with a painful past and a terrifying, feckless present. Could anyone compose polished poems and publishable short stories in such "uncertain" times?

Yes, it turned out, they could. We received hundreds of submissions from all over the D.C. area, as well as from writers and poets now far-flung but who were born here, or once worked or had an internship here, or went to school here—the stipulation was any personal, lived connection with Washington, D.C., Maryland, or Virginia, a region locally known as the DMV.

What came to us wasn't pretty—it was angry, eloquent, funny, visceral, raw, gorgeous, brilliant. You'll see. Winnowing *This Is What America Looks Like* down to just 111 poems and short stories was a feat, we don't mind saying. But from this embarrassment of riches, we chose the pieces that moved us the most, that shook us awake the most, that haunted our dreams the most. Here is WWPH's 2021 miracle.

Kathleen Wheaton
President
Washington Writers' Publishing House

Fiction Introduction

IF THERE HAD ONLY BEEN a pandemic, that would have been enough.

If there had only been an economic unraveling, that would have been enough.

If there had only been a racial reckoning, a social justice uprising, a need to say *their* names and to affirm that Black Lives Matter, that would have been more than enough.

Enough to write about for me, for us all, to fill one anthology, and perhaps many others.

However, as the pandemic hit and the world shut down, I wondered if we should continue, if we would have any writers submit, or if the work they submitted would be ragged with rage and anxiety. I wondered if the entire endeavor was hopeless. To my delight and amazement, I found more than 'enough' in the fiction that was submitted to *This Is What America Looks Like*: poetry and fiction from DC, Maryland and Virginia.

Many wrote what it looked like to live through a pandemic, but I was drawn to the unconventional point of view in Ofelia Montelongo's searing "Botones" as well as in Michelle Brafman's "I Am Your Mask" and Marcy Dilworth's "Last Night's Flight." Kay White Drew, a DC-area physician, on the other hand, takes a straight-on, unstoppable approach in "Front Lines."

Some took me on a journey to places I thought I knew well, notably Leslie Pietrzyk's dazzling moment of intense observation, "Admit This To No One," which is set around The White House. Some towns were discoveries: Peter Fortenbaugh's "Darce's Gift" hailing from Maryland's Eastern Shore and Ahmad Wright's "In My Own House," from rural Virginia. Both Fortenbaugh and Wright conceived haunting stories about funerals from their distinct perspectives.

Some stories break convention and bend genres—including the very last story accepted, Christopher J. Gregg's powerful "What I Read Between the Lines or a Prose Erasure of 'Executive Order on Building and Rebuilding Monuments to American Heroes.'"

Others immersed me in indelible voices, including Danielle Stonehirsch's

"Waffle House," Andrew Tran's "Garçon, Insurance," and the flash fiction dive from Myna Chang, wondrously titled "The Sky Stretches Clear and Whole for a Single, Hovering Heartbeat."

Stories that reflect the anger of our times, that seem to shout 'enough' at America, 'we should not look this way, but we do,' are also front and center here. "Spiraling" by Amy Freeman, "I'm Not Sorry," by Len Kruger, "In Lieu of Graduation 2020" by Garinè Isassi, and "ScrewNoDaddy" by Darlene Taylor are among these tightly wound, gut-punch stories.

Our own press members submitted, and for that I am grateful because their fiction writing shows the range and diversity of a press that I am so proud to be a member of now. And they are just such damn good writers: Robert J. Williams, Jacob R. Weber, Adam Schwartz, Patricia Schultheis, David Taylor, Nathan Leslie, Melanie S. Hatter and Elizabeth Bruce.

All of the stories are set in America, most in DC, Maryland and Virginia, and most in present day. One notable exception is the story that opens *This Is What America Looks Like* from the DC-writer Mary Kay Zuravleff—her achingly beautiful "Myrna, 1934." It felt so right to open with her story, for in order to look at who we are now, we must remember who we once were.

If there were only space to share insights on each of the thirty-eight short stories in this anthology, I would. I am thrilled, however, to share the work of all these writers with you. They give me hope.

Caroline Bock
Fiction Editor

Poetry Introduction

PUT YOUR EAR DOWN to the page and listen hard.

The poems included here are intentional and focused, and they engage with current conversations about the pandemic, mass incarceration, police violence, racial profiling, educational systems, aging, government policies/agendas, and gender/sexual expectations. Each of these conversations has its own particular history, and the poet has taken this conversation in image, metaphor, rhythm, narrative—the tools of the poet.

Many poems examine the ways in which these categories have been socially and hierarchically constructed to the benefit of some and to the disadvantage of others ("Sifting America's Garden," "American Progress," "Last Epistle"). Specifically, Cornelius Eady's poem, "Cops in Riot Gear Stormed a Violin Vigil for Elijah McClain," utters the last words of McClain as he was violently restrained by three police officers: "All I was trying to do was become better."

There are also poems here that are carried away by a particular place—a place and moment that highlights the America the poets know, which is often what the reader knows. These poems want you to lean in: Here is my America, my experience, is it yours? What do we share? How is it different? The poems explore the ugliness and the beauty. Donald Illich writes in "D.C.," "I'd never seen rats /crawl down city streets /until I came here, / where presidents lied, // and people knew / how to take the fifth." The poem "Called Back" by Jessica Garratt guides us through the Library of Congress, Kristin Ferragut's poem takes us to a county fair, Nancy Naomi Carlson leads us to Union Station, and "In the Beauty of the City" by current Maryland Poet Laureate Grace Cavalieri praises Dumbarton Oaks and "the glory of all this flowering."

Poets also explore the pandemic. The narrator in Myra Sklarew's poem "Co-ronavirus" speaks directly to the virus: "Some say you are not alive! // and [you] calmly disrupt the world!" Other poets have taken on the idea of our "new normal" when Elizabeth Knapp writes, "I admit I'm not quite ready for this, never / having adjusted to the old new normal." Linda Pastan's "The News of the Day" asserts "The green earth / is spinning / out of control." I am sure we would agree.

Boundaries—walls, gates, and doors are similarly traversed here ("There Must Be a Gate" and "The Invisible Walls"). Things that are built to separate us rather than join us. Many poems speak to and complicate questions of identity and immigration. In Mauricio Novoa's "Soil," he writes, "Mami's dreams of becoming / a teacher stopped at the tip / of the corn husk." Regie Cabico tells us that "I survived the American dream / deferred in the loss of a mother / who thought Lady Liberty / would be this beach she saw / watching Hollywood films."

The last poem in the anthology, "The Circus is Here" by Fran Abrams asks, "Why would anyone go to the circus anymore?" True. Since the narrator tells us, "If you want to see people die, / watch the news." The poets here blur and often redefine the lines of American myths and ideals, problems and challenges. The poetry in this anthology is a hallmark of our time and our place as poets in this part of the country.

They're about listening, and listening to each other.

Jona Colson
Poetry Editor

Myrna, 1934

MARY KAY ZURAVLEFF

MA WANTED ME to give up my crib for the new baby—didn't I want the new baby to have a bed? Didn't I want to be a big girl?

Every time I got in my crib, I touched the little sleeping lamb above my head. Her wool was painted as a field of white with black curlicues that I moved my finger around. Her long eyelashes were how I learned to count. She had four on one eye and five on the other, or as many as all but my thumb on one eye and my whole hand on the other. I didn't ask for a new baby, although I liked the idea of being bigger than someone in the house.

Hazel was so big she was grown up. She had a job washing dishes in the hospital kitchen. Tommy was even bigger, but he wasn't grown. Ma was always telling him stories about a young man, as in, "A young man covers hisself, even indoors," or "A young man flushes after he makes." She didn't tell Luke these stories, though he was younger than Tommy. I was the youngest. I was the baby.

My crib was in Ma and Pa's room, though Pa wasn't there anymore. He lived in our front room, in a bed, in a tent. Hazel mostly slept with Ma because the sofa where she used to sleep was pushed against the wall to make space for Pa. His tent fit over his bed. There was a big red tank that gave him good air. The tent kept the good air in.

Pa couldn't go to work, or go look for work. He couldn't go to church, because the smoke Father Timofei waved around got him coughing. Even before Pa went in the tent, he skipped a lot of church. His lungs were black from the years he was a miner in the town where Ma grew up. Her ma and pa were from the same town in Russia that Pa was. They'd all gotten on boats for America to dig up coal.

The other day, Father Timofei came to our house without his smoke. He chanted prayers as Ma and the rest of us crossed ourselves and touched the ground. Pa crossed himself in his tent.

On weekdays, Luke and Hazel came home at the end of Lux Radio Theater. Ma fed us all lunch, and then Luke went back to school and Hazel went back to the hospital. That's when Tommy and I had to rest. Because Ma's lap was full of the next baby, she sat by my crib and read to me. I stretched myself out so long that I pushed my feet against the slats at the bottom of my crib and my head against the slats at the top. All I really had that was mine was Brownie and my crib. I knew cribs were for babies, so if we had a baby, the baby should sleep in the crib.

Then this morning, I woke up already thinking, thinking, thinking, until—*pop!*—I figured it out, just like in the funny pages, when a light bulb comes on over someone's noggin, and their eyes bug out. I pushed the side of my crib down and climbed out. I ran in my nightie and socks to where Ma was in the kitchen making the men's sandwiches. And it was still early, because the men hadn't picked up their drawstrings yet and Hazel and the boys were still asleep.

Ma and Pa used to make lunches together, and Pa used to deliver them to the rooming house on his way to the stove factory. Before he was in the tent, he used to bring home the men's lunch money, and he and Ma danced around the kitchen, shaking the coins in a coffee can.

Ma had two rows of bread slices set out like a card game. I knew Pa's part well enough to dip a knife in the mustard for the top row. Ma crossed herself, because I'd surprised her, though I hadn't meant to be sneaky. She said, "Who would have thought my blinchiki could help so?"

Her praise shamed me a little, like I'd been pretending to be a baby when I could have been pitching in. I took the stack of cheese she'd sliced, and I dealt one, two squares on top of each mustard bread. She usually flitted around the table like a moth, but the baby made her sit in a chair. "You know just what's what," she said and set a liverwurst circle on each cheese square.

That's when I told her my idea. I would give the baby my crib if I could move into Pa's tent with him. "He's always having to rest, and I still nap. He can't work, and school won't take me yet." Ma was shaking her head, which made me speed up. I said, "His tank is great big huge. I'm little, so I don't need much air."

"Myrna, Myrna, Myrna," Ma said. She always purred my name like that when she was about to let me down.

Ma wrapped the sandwiches in paper like little presents. I brought her the stack of drawstrings. They were different front and back because she sewed them from leftovers, with a string through them you drew closed. I spotted scraps from housedresses she'd made for Baba and Aunt Sonya, who still lived in the mines. I stroked a bag that had been Pa's checked shirt and my old nightie.

I said, "Here's how I'd breathe in the tent." I puffed air, chugging like the little engine that could, which she read me.

"Myrna," Ma couldn't stop saying.

I promised to leave Brownie in the crib for the new baby. That was a bonus I thought of on the spot. Ma could wake me up in the tent when it was time to make lunches. I'd get up and mustard the bread every day.

I put one apple into each drawstring and didn't know I was talking until Ma said, "Stop jabbering." She stood still, so I froze, too. Pa was making a racket. Usually he started up like Uncle Kostia's car, sputtering. His tent plugged in and hummed, so he had to be hacking pretty loud for Ma and me to hear him in the kitchen.

Ma wiped her hands on her apron, way out in front of her because of the baby. In my stocking feet, I slid on the wood floor right past her and saw Pa through the clear window of his tent. He'd raised himself on one arm and was tilting over the side of his bed. Ma had set a tin pan on the floor, and Pa's spit hit the pan like acorns on our roof. I'd never sneaked a peek at Pa first thing in the morning. His face was gray as flannel, and blood spotted his nightshirt.

Pa slept in a tent instead of his bed. I knew that. But I'd been thinking of him cozy in there the way we were in the blanket-and-chair forts we made on rainy days. The way I was in my crib. Seeing his wet pink eyes, I tugged at the zipper to get to him. When I peeled opened the flap, a dead-chicken smell came out, like when Aunt Pearl visited. She'd give Ma a newspaper package, saying "Just wrung its neck." Pa's neck was all wrinkly, and black whiskers were starting to poke out of his skin like pin feathers. He tried to talk, which sent him into another fit.

Ma gave me a shove. "*Bystreye!*"

I got a running start and then slid along the wood floor to the kitchen linoleum. I dragged the stepstool from under the sink so I could reach a cup and turned on the tap. I climbed down the stepstool with Pa's water. When I got to the wood floor this time, I tried not to slide. On the long short walk to Pa's tent, I held the cup in one hand and stuck out my other arm. That's what tightrope walkers did at the Armory Circus, where Pa took me and Luke to celebrate the job before the stove factory. I spilled a little, and watching the water in the cup made me spill more. I remembered Pa told me that tightrope walkers stare at the spot where they want to go and don't look down.

Ma unzipped the tent flap the rest of the way and got Pa's shirt off. She propped the Pa pillow behind his back to raise him up. Ma had made the Pa pillow, which looked like a puffy doorstop, a big wedge, and Ma said even Pa's doctor told her it was clever. From the spout of the red tank, a long thin straw went to Pa's nose, stuck down with tape across his moustache. Either Pa wasn't as gray as he'd been or I'd gotten used to him. He looked more like himself, except his bare chest reminded me of Mr. Bones, the skeleton in the back of Murphy's Drugstore.

Luke used to scare me with stories of Mr. Bones leaving Murphy's at night and walking up Parade Street to our house. "You hear him? Now?" he'd ask, and I was sure he was rattling up the porch steps to throttle me.

Ma guided Pa's arms through a clean shirt, and Pa rested a palm on her belly as she buttoned him up. I saw the baby kick them both. When Pa let go of her belly to take the cup from me, his hand sloshed the water from rim to rim.

The knob in Pa's neck bobbed up and down as he sipped and swallowed. He took longer breaths with just the starts of coughs—Kik! Kik! Kik!—and was able to smother them, though once he leaned over and spit blood into the bucket. He sipped more water, which settled him.

When he could take a breath without coughing, he whispered, "That's the stuff, Blinchiki."

"She helped make the lunches," Ma said.

"You are my big girl," Pa whispered.

My head filled with questions, most of which I knew not to ask. *If I sleep in here, can I take care of you?* was one. *Can I have your tent if you die?* was another. *Are you ever going to get out of bed so we can skip stones on the lake?*

I thought I'd figured out an answer but all I had now were questions. *What if the new baby doesn't get to meet you? What if it does and you love it more than me? What if you give it my crib and call it your Blinchiki?*

Ma scooted over a little bit, and her belly pushed me aside. "Pa needs to rest hisself now," she said. "You can see what's what."

Pa whispered, "Thanks for the city juice," and handed me the cup with his bony hand. His hands had always been bony, but they didn't used to rattle. The air going in his nose through the tube may as well have been water the way his breath gurgled. I wanted to ask, *why does blood come out your mouth? Why do you need different air than us?*

I wanted to crawl into the tent with him, but I also wanted to make him tea and black bread with butter and honey, the way he liked. I'd figured out what to do about my crib, but what I remember is that inside my head, baby was washing out and big girl was flooding in, and truly I thought I might drown.

In My Own Home

AHMAD WRIGHT

"POP DON'T WANT to be buried here," Karo said.

The shovel's wood handle chaffed Karo's palms. Roots and rocks twisted the soil strata and interrupted Karo's flow. He was not allowed to wear gloves or use a pickaxe to break the rocks. He had the same shovel his father used when he buried his own grandfather, and so on, as the story goes. Nothing but sweat and body, the natural machine. Digging strained Karo's back. Why wouldn't it? Funeral shoes ruined, face muddy. When he stopped digging, it was because he wished for relief from the noon heat that tree shade couldn't give. His contribution to the day's affair: a two-hour flight to Richmond, an hour drive to Goochland, and five hours of digging——all within 24 hours. His funeral tux was damp, shirt untucked, soiled, and wet to the skin. Momma had his jacket. Uncle Tick had his tie.

The funeral director was the preacher, the mayor, and Karo's old high school coach; the old man unfastened the last button on his suit and knelt to extend his hand to Karo, helping him out of the three-foot ditch.

"Pop didn't even want to be buried back here in the yard," Karo said again. "He told me."

"Buried by your hand in the yard, Karo. It's what is written. Family tradition. Buried in this yard with his people. Period,"

The old man's build was slight now, muscle replaced by the slack and grit of routine. His heavy face could have been a sack of black beans.

Karo wiped his cheek on his sleeve as he followed the funeral director ahead of him.

Prayers were done, and Karo couldn't remember the hymn his sister picked. A few mourners had stuck around while he dug the plot—the hole was almost finished.

The funeral director continued shaking hands, conversing in the language of final business. A long line of matriarchs in wide-brimmed hats and seam dresses met his smile and clenched his wrist with both hands.

Bless you!

Amen!

He's with God now!

The elderly women shuffled into the house rocking to a song only they could hear. The men followed their wives, their suits and skin gleaning. They nodded at the funeral director. No talking. Nothing left to see. Karo stepped over the fresh mounds of earth to get closer to the departing crowd.

"I hear the repast is a bounty, Karo," the funeral director said. "Your sister did good. Your family's inside."

"Who are all these people?"

"The town," the funeral director said. "You been gone a few years. Some remember you."

He patted Karo on the shoulder.

The inside of the house had not changed. Wood floors and deep-set rooms; miniature framed photos of ancestors—*not ours!* Pop liked to be reminded of where he came from, so he collected photos of black workers. *Not slaves,* he would say. The whiff of fried fish filled the main room and hallway. Marmalade jelly on the fancy plates floated hand to hand to well-wishers whispering with their mouths full. Karo followed the line of guests to the half kitchen where his baby sister loaded food on paper plates as her husband, Ray, passed them out.

"You finished digging? You going to clean up?"

She didn't turn around to greet him, but she knew he was there. The sleeves of her funeral dress were cinched at the elbow, mom's apron around the neck and tied around the waist. "Bathroom still out the hallway to the right. Use soap." They shared the same ears, heavy arms, same skinny neck. "You really come back. Had dibs you wasn't."

"Don't save me a plate," Karo said, fixed on the back of her big head. Braids sill didn't hide it.

Ray sifted to the front of the line with open arms balancing full paper plates of food. The line moved faster than he could serve.

"Karo, good to see you, man." He handed the last two plates of fish on his arm to the next guests in line. "C'mon here."

He led Karo out of the kitchen into the hallway. Ray was taller by a good six inches, heavier by fifty pounds. God meant for his unibrow to replace the mustache, but there it was, catching a receding hairline instead.

"You're staying?" Ray asked. He was the only one not dressed in funeral colors but rather work boots, a blue jean shirt, and coveralls so deep brown dirt didn't show as much. Ray used to be in his middle school homeroom and dressed the same now as an adult in all of the photos that Karo received from his parents, always lurking in the background like an unpainted wall.

That was ten years ago.

"Your daddy gave me my first job at the hardware store, Karo."

"Sorry I missed the wedding."

"We own the store now," Ray paused. "Your sister said you wouldn't want it. Didn't want that on your mind with this funeral stuff. He's going to be right beside his folks and their folks," he said, rehearsing the preacher's directions. "You dug a good plot for him so far."

Karo tucked his shirt, smoothed his sleeves, "Pop wanted to be cremated. And he didn't like parties."

Down the hall he could see a crowd swelling in the main room. Women sat and ate together. Men stood in groups eating with their hands. The preacher entered and motioned his arms.

Karo stepped ahead of Ray closer to crowd. Many people nodded but said nothing. Mom shared a plate of fish with Uncle Tick, who never shared anything. She offered the rest of his tux, the jacket to cover the messed-up shirt, the tie because today should be the one time he wears one.

Karo waved her away.

"Take the jacket and tie," the preacher said. He pulled a dirty shovel from behind his back. "Take this, too. Finish the job."

Trail Walk

ROBERT J. WILLIAMS

A CRISP BREEZE swept over the Metropolitan Branch Trail. LaShawn tilted his head back—his dreadlocks raining—and poured Cheeto crumbs into his mouth. He chewed wildly and tossed the empty bag onto the trail pavement, but immediately thought better. "See that. That's evidence. Five seconds of some CSI shit and these fools got my records from ten years back up on a screen. Next thing you know, I'm a suspect for one of these robberies that's been happening. All this technology is just making it harder for a nigga to live carefree."

Carefree hit David like a bow-tied gift. Word surprises were one of the reasons David liked hanging with LaShawn. Big brother figure. Giver of advice. And weedman to him and the other white prep schoolboys who convened at Union Station before their late afternoon commutes back home. David had first met LaShawn on the Metro station's platform, second semester, sophomore year. LaShawn spotted him standing silent and apart from a gaggle of toothy Bethesda-bound lacrosse jocks, their sticks secured behind their backs like battle swords. "You smoke?" LaShawn asked, not bothering for a response after he spotted a copy of *Fahrenheit 451* peeking out of David's backpack. "Bradbury. You reading that? Shit's dope."

From that day on, LaShawn supplied David with freebies here and there while they lingered around the Metro entrance to chat about science fiction reads and gamer shit, or trade Soundcloud links of favorite underground rappers. LaShawn was easy to talk to, wore no armor like the few Black guys David knew from school. Funny, since LaShawn had more hard luck life markers than any of them: incarcerated uncles, a blind grandmother taking him into her house when he was nine, being nabbed by MPD at fifteen for some bullshit food court altercation that got out of hand. On his own at eighteen. At least that's the way

LaShawn dripped his life story during those after-school meetups and occasional escapes to the nearby trail to talk and smoke, inhaled weed spurring delivery of random words like *carefree*. He alternately thanked and blamed childhood boredom, overreaching school teachers, and a few years of working in downtown mailrooms for his expansive worldview and vocabulary choices. David knew LaShawn was just innately a different guy. And maybe his only real friend, too.

David chased and picked up the fleeing Cheeto bag and stuffed it into the back pocket of his wrinkled khakis, the lower half of his school uniform.

"Good job, little brother," LaShawn said. "Now that joint hosting both our DNA. We better get moving. Two idle niggas on this path is too much cause for suspicion. Remember that. Keep it kinetic."

David hearing himself being called the N-word triggered a hard tongue swallow. He couldn't ever show any affinity for it and certainly couldn't say *it* aloud himself—those were the rules, on the trail and off. But he'd try to shape a verbalization in his head, perfecting intonation, making sure *not* to sound like his Uncle Stu. Whenever he drank, Uncle Stu would grow chatty and inevitably unwind the story of his dismissal from Maryland's state police force. Some vindictive *nigger* boss didn't like him, he'd say, plunging into a pool of self-pity. The middle *g's* and ending *r* were hit hard, fired like rounds at a shooting range. David's mom would shush Uncle Stu, but he'd pay her no mind. David wanted to enunciate the word like LaShawn did: natural, rhythmic, friendly, comforting. Cool. But only in his head. David practiced mentally: *Niiiggah. Nee-guh. N'g'a. N'kuh.* David's brain gave up. Once again, he'd never get it right.

Time had slipped away. It was later than the usual hour David hung out with LaShawn. The trail's overhead lights flickered on, dutifully and robotically. "The city be making things nice when y'all started moving in," LaShawn said, observing all the bulbs actually worked. He amended that he knew long ago the surrounding neighborhood was called Swampoodle and had been home to Irish immigrants in the 1800s. "Shit get fancy with a quickness when y'all come back. Even after more than a hundred years. But then a few robberies make the news, and all of sudden they get worried again, start fearing every passing nigga reminding them of the bad old days. Their fears trump my freedom." A young white couple approached, the man in running shorts but not running, the woman pushing a stroller. Neither made eye contact with David or LaShawn as they passed. LaShawn levered a thumb over his shoulder. "Exhibit A. That's going to be you, David, after you finish college, and one day finally learn how to talk to girls, marry one and get a good job. Ten years, you and yours see me coming in the opposite direction, your fingers will be itching to call 911." LaShawn shook his head. "Watch."

LaShawn jabbed David in the chest. Hard. David absorbed a sharp pain that wormed about his insides, feeling it was deserved. In ten years, if all went to plan, that *would* be him. But his future self would speak to LaShawn. He would even still be his friend. Maybe they'd still be taking afternoon strolls together, splitting cruddy joints before long commutes to their respective homes.

"You finished all your college applications yet?" LaShawn asked. A female jogger appeared, running breathlessly and awkwardly. Her skinny bones hit the trail pavement hard. Her face showed pain. LaShawn shook his head. "Your people, son. Never understand why they love running if it's so torturous to them."

"Still working on the personal essays," David redirected. His college applications had been crowding his mind all week. He wanted to talk about that, not theorize about why so many white girls ran. "I thought I might write one about you. *Us*. Us being friends. That's got to be a topic that would make me stand out from every other white boy from Montgomery County applying to Hopkins and Brown. Shit, maybe even Villanova."

LaShawn laughed. "What's the thesis of this proposed essay?"

David shrugged. "In progress."

"Let me guess. How we all the same on the inside? How once you get to know people, color don't matter? How we all have the same fears and basic human needs?"

David felt embarrassed, regretting bringing up his topic idea. But he knew LaShawn wouldn't let go, at least until his mind veered into another pathway. "It'd be about how you can learn from anybody if you open your ears and listen. That's what I hope to be in college. You know, open-minded."

"Ah. Now a nigga is *anybody*. What's the title going to be: *Life Lessons from My Nigga LaShawn?*" LaShawn fingered an imaginary keyboard. "Might work. For Brown. Possibly. Not Hopkins, though." He retrieved a smudgy joint from a plastic bag that had been in his jeans pocket. He lit it and savored a long first hit. Weed was visually medicinal for LaShawn. *Gas* he called it. His natural flinty glare softened when he smoked, transforming his eyes into those of a poet or artist juggling inner thoughts, piecing together ideas for a new project. He handed the joint to David. "Tell you what, little brother. You want to write about me? Us? Let's run a little experiment to give you some insight about *us*. Next random white person we see on this trail, I'll run up on them a little anxious like, but then ask them something *innocuous*. Like the time or directions or some shit.

Then the one after that, you'll do the same and see what reaction you get. Let's see how color blind and same-on-the-inside they think we are."

David shook his head, feeling an ominous pinch scale his neck. "No need to prove anything, man. I know what you're trying to say."

"Do you?" Two people on bikes passed first, helmeted and pedaling too fast to get their attention. A minute later, another white woman jogged around the trail bend. Earbuds lodged into her ears, she ran in a rhythmic stride. Her thigh muscle tensed as she accelerated. She looked to have been a serious athlete, an erstwhile field hockey or soccer player, David presumed.

LaShawn emerged from the trail edge and planted himself in the middle of the pavement. He raised an open hand towards the woman. Her speed increased to a full-on sprint. As her face came into view, David could see her steely stare. When the woman was yards away and seemed to be making no effort to stop or cut or curve, LaShawn recoiled as if trying to elude a runaway train. Losing his footing, he fell backwards. The woman didn't flinch. Unbothered, she continued her run. LaShawn rubbed his head as if he had taken a blow.

David helped LaShawn up from the pavement. "Dude, are you crazy? What was the point? She could have had mace, could have screamed. Things could have escalated real quick. Lucky she ignored your ass."

"But what if all I needed really was some directions?" LaShawn asked. "Them always the odds for me, little brother. You went straight to the most extreme thing she could have done, and you're right. That's the way we got to think every day. Had you been out there, she might have stopped at least. The odds you get are in your favor. Wasn't but one of three things was going to happen for me, two of them bad. One of them *really* bad. Me, I got to stay paranoid like. Let's see what happens to you with the next one."

"Nah," David said. "It's stupid. Besides, it's no longer a good experiment. The next white woman that passes is a different variable. There's no telling if she would do the same thing. You're making it sound like all white women are alike, think the same things and react the same way. That's not fair. Your experiment is dumb."

David took a hit of the joint to calm himself. He and LaShawn had had disagreements before over silly stuff, but never a real argument.

Another runner approached from the opposite direction. An athletic woman, Black, she was wearing spandex and a large oversized sweatshirt adorned with a seal of some sort. She accelerated as she neared David and LaShawn. David shielded the joint as the woman got close.

"How you doing, ma'am?" David said as the woman's curious eyes danced between him and LaShawn. "Nice evening, yes?" David felt nervous, like the woman might be a cop, not just another runner on the trail. The woman sneered and said nothing. She then held her nose as she sped through the weed aroma lingering about. Her trot quickened, but she managed to look back and fire another look of disgust at David. When the woman reached a point out of earshot, David burst into laughter.

"White, Black, blue or green, seems no woman is stopping for pleasant conversation with a pair of shady dudes blazing on a dark trail, no matter what we look like. And they're probably right to think so, for their own safety. I don't blame them. Everything isn't always black and white, and it's not always about Black and white." David took a quick last hit, knowing he'd better head home before his mom started calling. "So, professor, what's your conclusion on the findings of this experiment?" he asked.

Riding the Saw

JACOB R. WEBER

IT HADN'T RAINED IN DAYS, which made it easy for Theodore to pull his small body through the cordgrass along the stream without his bare feet sticking in the mud. The grass was taller than he was, and brittle, so it whipped at his face and ears. Even his father, Friedrich, winced as he forced his way through it with his shoulders, which were hard and triangular like ax blades. Each time he shoved, the grass would bend to make room for him, but as soon as he passed, it would snap back at Theodore. Friedrich heard his son's panting interrupted now and again by gasps of irritation, but he was already carrying the saw and would do no more than break trail to help his son.

The boy was six and should be near the age when he wanted to prove to his father and his brothers that he could do more, could carry the saw himself or feed the chickens at dusk without fear of bears as long as he had the Winchester with him. His brothers' hair had turned brown by the time they were his age, but Theodore's was still the color of the ashes Friedrich had known in Pennsylvania.

He hurried the boy along by increasing his own pace. Theodore would not want to be left behind so near the dark of the trees. It wasn't much of a forest, but the trunks were dark and could suck the light out of the early May sun twenty feet in, forest enough for an imagination like his. He could make a dragon out of a dishpan.

Two swamp sparrows burst out of the fox hedge Theodore was stuck in beside the stream, and the boy ducked. Friedrich flipped the saw from left hand to right and picked out a path to the oaks. Theodore pulled himself from the muck and dashed forward until he was even with his father. Flies clouded Theodore's head, but they let taller Friedrich be.

On the edge of the woods was the oak Friedrich had felled last week with Cletus, one of his older sons. Without a word, he set the teeth of the saw across the trunk and took his handle, waiting for Theodore to take his. When Theodore took in an exaggerated breath to rest from his walk, Friedrich squeezed until his thumb crotch swelled around the brown nibs and set his jaw hard.

He allowed his son a few test runs across the tree to get the groove started and find his rhythm. He was too choppy on the backstroke, pulling too hard and up, following the natural inclination to yank it out of the hole, like a hatchet stuck in a tree.

"You can't treat a bucksaw like a butter churn," he told the boy.

Stroke by stroke, Theodore learned. The groove grew deeper, and like magic what was solid turned to dust, then to emptiness. When the last splinters were all that held the piece they'd cut to the rest of the trunk, Friedrich quit sawing and kicked the rest away with his boot.

"We need a few more. Your mama's doing up the sheets today as well as the cooking."

They set to cutting the next log, the boy no longer breathing heavily but entranced by the alchemy of the tree that seemed to melt slowly in front of him. Friedrich watched him through his good eye. The child was still pale but had gotten some color back since his winter flu. They'd all had it bad for a while, but not like some. He was grateful he'd built the chicken coop big enough for so many chickens. When he'd put it up, he'd planned to sell eggs to the folks in town. But when the banks had run out of money, the town had nothing to buy with. Augustus Hecht, who owned the bank, had been found floating one morning in the Illinois River, though his widow refused to admit it had been a suicide. The chickens Friedrich had meant to sell had become the family's life raft; they ate eggs twice a day and chicken twice a week. The bank was open again now, and if folks ever put money back in it, the family would all live to say they never wanted to eat another egg as long as they lived. In the meantime, they'd never had to beg, or steal, which was more than some people could say. It wasn't just bears who came to the coop at night.

The second log fell faster than the first; the third was faster still. They would only need a few more. They might not be able to carry all the logs along with the saw, but no matter. He'd send Cletus to get the rest. Theodore had nearly done enough for today. As he set the teeth for another run, he said again, with a good deal more gusto than the first time, "You can't treat a bucksaw like a butter churn!"

He wondered sometimes if he was too hard on the boy. His own father had done much worse, and his grandfather would probably have killed one of his own sons eventually if scarlet fever hadn't taken all his strength. But that didn't mean Friedrich had to pass that on. He could let it wither away, like wood disappeared into sawdust, and then nothing.

Then he heard an exaggerated puff of breath again from Theodore. The boy kept going. A little later, another huff. Ever so slightly, he felt the tug on the saw go slack. The boy was riding the saw, letting his father do the work while he just kept his hands on and pretended to pull. Friedrich regretted having considered for a moment going easy on the boy. His sayings, his thoughts, these things were no deeper than the little strip of forest the boy was so afraid to go into. As if knowing what was about to happen, a flock of swamp sparrows burst from the trees and shot off toward wherever it seemed fit to them to go.

Friedrich yanked the saw from the groove, snatching it from Theodore and taking it back behind him with both hands. He flung it toward his son. It would hit him or he would duck. Either way, the boy would learn a lesson, the most important lesson Friedrich had to teach. Either way, he would soon pack up and head back to the house, carrying as much with him as he could.

Sifting America's Garden

NABEELA WASHINGTON

After the pronouncement
and cries of rage
and several calls
and transportation of the body.

After the body is tagged
and bullets extracted
and organs discarded
and insides further ravaged.

After the gloves are tossed
sorry for your loss
and the coffin is picked
and body fitted.

After it's tucked beneath soil
and protests expire
and whimpers grow faint
and aches are suppressed.

After the body has settled
and ephemerals spring forth
and visitors frisk the tomb
where stolen Black bodies are planted,

a community yearns to breathe again.

The Lucky Ones

NORAH VAWTER

ANOTHER DINNERTIME. And once again, I found myself under the table. At eight years old, I was getting well acquainted with the intricately patterned rug my father swore at every time he pushed my mother's wheelchair up to the dining room table. It was the sort of rug that looked like wall-to-wall carpet, but it didn't attach to anything, not the wall, not the floor. The rug bunched up under the chair's wheels, and snagged, and made everyone angry. That night I stared at the ridges of that rug, at the ripples no one could make lie flat. The designs on the rug looked like faces. For just a moment, the shooter's face appeared, empty, blank, but brutal, as he raised his gun for the first shot. The stranger who'd attacked my mother and me in broad daylight, on a busy street, when I was four. Back when we lived in New Orleans. Dirty, stumbling, he'd appeared to be homeless, maybe on drugs or mentally ill. Since he'd never been caught, this man loomed large in my imagination, and so even now I saw his face everywhere.

At the table, my mother sat in her wheelchair, choking and aspirating. This was my grandfather's fancy, stuffy dining room. Two years before, when I was six years old, he'd finally worn my father, Max, down, forced us to move up to New England after my mother got out of rehab, to live here with him like poor relations. My mother, Rose, had grown up in this small town on the Massachusetts coast, in this very house. My grandmother had died the summer before the shooting, leaving Pop Pop to live here alone until we showed up. For the past twenty minutes, Mina had been rushing around, sending my father and grandfather to get washcloth after washcloth for Rose to spit up into. This happened a couple times a week. I was always supposed to keep eating while my mother coughed and choked and sounded like death. I always tried to sit there like nothing was wrong, tried to eat my food despite the noise and flurry of activity, but I never lasted more than a few minutes. Try as I might, I always ended up under the table, as if propelled down there by an outside force.

When they weren't running around, my dad and grandfather managed to eat the jambalaya Max had prepared for dinner. I could see their legs from my place on the floor. Max kept jostling his knee up and down like he was nervous. In contrast, Pop Pop's knees were clamped tightly together, a white linen napkin placed carefully on his lap. Every so often, he picked up the napkin with a calm, smooth motion, presumably to blot sauce off his lips. All through dinner, Pop Pop kept peeking underneath the table. Glaring at me. He looked like he was going to tear his hair out, bit by bit, if I didn't start acting like an honest-to-god young lady. Eventually, up went his head, and soon his feet scurried out of the room. More washcloths.

This was why I never invited anybody for dinner, not even my best friend. I felt stuck to the dining room floor. It was as if the combined force of choking and aspirating and hospitals and quadriplegia and adults and that awful sound when Rose couldn't catch her breath—it was as if that force had pushed me off my seat, down to the carpet. I couldn't move. I couldn't take my hands off my ears. I couldn't breathe. I couldn't stop crying. I couldn't look at this rationally. And I definitely couldn't chew up bites of sausage and rice, swallow them, and keep them down while my mother all but threw up her dinner.

In our new reality, everything was complicated for my mother: getting up in the morning, signing a check, reading a book, or even eating dinner. While chewing and swallowing her food, my mother often got tiny bits of it stuck in her breathing passage, which ended up in her lungs and made her choke (aspiration, I was told). The real problem with aspirating was that when Rose had tiny particles of food caught in her lungs, bacteria could be attached to the bits of food. Bacteria led to infections. Infections led to pneumonia. Pneumonia meant the hospital. Again. I'd been lucky during the shooting—she'd thrown her body on top of me, and I'd escaped with nothing but a collapsed lung and surface wounds, out of the hospital in a week, no permanent physical injuries. Rose had not been lucky.

Now, as I heard her cough and spit up, my whole body tightened. I remembered that hospital smell—antiseptics and death. I imagined a coffin. The hospital was never over. Every few months, she'd end up in a hospital, almost die, only to emerge pink and weak like a newborn baby. The doctors continued to be confused by her recovery. Against all odds, she kept coming home to us. But at some point, the odds had to win over my mother's stubbornness and my dad's almost magical confidence.

"Watson," my grandfather snapped, using my father's last name like it was a warning. "Get Anna Rose off the floor! She'll listen to you. Just get her to sit at the table."

"There you go, Rosie," Mina said, her voice a mixture of warmth and firmness as Rose went into another coughing fit. "Almost got it all."

"See?" Pop Pop said. "She's almost done. So get Anna Rose up from my carpet and into her seat before my daughter gets upset and starts coughing again."

Max's knee jiggled almost violently. Then it was still. Somehow, even though I could only see his legs, I knew his whole body had gone still. That he was wiping his hands clean with his napkin. "You've got to be crazy. She's just a kid. And it's nobody's fault when someone chokes," my dad said in a cool, collected voice. "Anna, you're excused. Go upstairs. Go outside. Go anywhere you like. But you are excused from dinner."

I stayed where I was. I felt sure that if I let go of my knees, my body might just float away.

"She is not excused," Pop Pop snapped, his voice flustered and hot. Rose went into another coughing fit. I could hear Mina helping her, and making soothing sounds. The men's argument continued over the coughing and aspirating. I closed my eyes and pressed my face into my knees.

Eventually, Max climbed under the table and laid his hand on my shoulder. "Honey," he whispered kindly. "Let's get you out of here."

I couldn't move. I couldn't open my eyes. My body shook with deep, heaving sobs. I couldn't move. I couldn't look at him. I couldn't do anything but cry. While everyone had been ignoring me, I'd managed to keep myself quiet. But now that my father was trying to fix things, I couldn't stay quiet. I couldn't keep myself intact. Max squeezed my shoulder. "I'm sorry I let it go this far," he murmured. "But I'm getting you out of here. And this is never happening again." He pulled me towards him, folding my body into his. "Goddamn," he said as he hit his head on the table.

"Language!" Pop Pop snapped.

Then I heard my mother's voice. She'd stopped choking. "Anna Rose," my mother croaked. "It's okay, love. It's over."

Her voice was different from her voice before the shooting. Her words sounded like they'd been rubbed in sandpaper. Each word strained and breathy, as if she were always moaning and groaning.

Max hadn't managed to get me out from under the table yet. I tried to stop crying. I really did. I glanced at Max, his face tired and worn but determined. I reached out to feel his scratchy salt-and-pepper beard. He whispered, "I got you, kiddo."

"Anna Rose," Rose pleaded.

Mina shushed all of us as she said, "Now, Rose, I figure part of the problem was the rice. Too small. Let's remember that, you hear me? Rice is not for you anymore."

Somehow Mina's voice helped calm my whole body. She sounded so matter-of-fact, like this was a purely logistical problem, just something she had to tackle on the job. I relaxed into my father's arms. Max stroked my long black hair, which hung halfway down my back.

"It's not the rice," Rose muttered.

"Now that you mention it, it'd help if you stopped yapping during dinner, and when it's time to chew, you gotta keep your chin down like I showed you," Mina kept on, all business now. "Now, please. Let me help you with your dinner." I could hear Rose chewing. Then asking for a sip of water.

Max wrapped his arms around me. He was a slight man, but his arms felt strong, solid. I felt a flood of kindness flow into me. I let myself collapse in his arms. I breathed in his scent: cigarettes and cheap cologne. Finally he pulled me out from under the dining room table.

I couldn't help but look at Rose. A seat belt of sorts held her onto the wheelchair by wrapping around her chest and fastening behind her back. Both her arms were stuck in a strange position: they were perpetually bent, and her elbows pointed straight out, as if she were dancing the funky chicken. She wore a baggy green sweater, which she would never have worn in her old life. Her sweater did match her eyes, its green like apple green but softer. Yet it hung on her body in such an unflattering way. She was skinnier than ever, but those chicken wing arms just would not fit into her old clothes. Mina often sliced the back of her blouses open to fit them on my mother's odd shape. The bullets hadn't just paralyzed Rose. They'd made her frumpy.

Yet somehow she was still beautiful. Her hair still the orangey-red of a sunset, not a hint of gray. She looked exhausted, face red from all the choking—but she smiled at me, her expression full of embarrassment and desperate hope. I tried to smile at my mother—my new mother, my wrong mother. This imposter who wore Rose's broken body and spoke with her broken soul. I smiled, like I always tried to. I pulled my chair out, getting ready to sit down.

Max, standing behind me, put his hands on both my shoulders. "You're excused," he said.

"Watson," my grandfather snapped. Pop Pop hadn't gotten up from his chair at the head of the table. Now, he methodically wiped his hands on his napkin, though his hands seemed perfectly clean to begin with. He was a large man—taller than my father, and you could tell it even when he was sitting down—with broad shoulders and an imposing look about him.

"Come on, Jim," Max said, his voice light. "Let the kid go play. The rest of us should get back to the jambalaya. Let's all remember I made this from scratch, and I got the recipe from my buddy who runs the kitchen at K-Paul's in the Quarter. Rosie knows him, don't you, sweetheart?"

My mother smiled. "Cannot be his recipe. He was going to take it to his grave or something else melodramatic."

Max chuckled, saying, "How would you know? You were busy choking on the rice. But Mina's right. Just eat the sausage and vegetables. That's the good part anyway. Right, Anna?" He squeezed my shoulders. Rose actually laughed.

I moved to sit down. I could be the kid they all wanted me to be. But I took another look at my broken mother, at this whole broken dinner table scene. I didn't have the words for this yet, but deep in my bones, I knew there was something rotten in that dining room. It wasn't normal, it shouldn't be, but they were trying to pretend like it was. Every cell in my body was telling me to not sit down. To not give in. To propel myself somewhere else. It wasn't enough to get off the floor.

I left my seat at the table empty, giving them one last look before I ran from the room.

Garçon, Insurance

ANDREW TRAN

I WAS CONCERNED ABOUT EVERYTHING and concerned about nothing. As I sat on my front porch and drank a cup of black coffee mixed with oat milk, I was figuring out how my brain worked. I had severe depression and anxiety, and I was just learning how to cope. I left my front porch and went into my house. I walked upstairs to the second floor and went into my bedroom, climbed out of the window, and stepped onto the rooftop. I laid my back down on the rough shingle tops and soaked up the bright sunlight, knowing even if I would never figure out the meaning of life, at least I had my drawbacks. I was sleep-deprived and looking into the sky, trying to see if there were angels flying around the cluster of clouds. No angels dropped down from the clouds, which made me disappointed. Not a single bird flew by either. I was nineteen years old and I believed in communism, but I was also Vietnamese American, which gave my belief system irony. And then I realized I was lying to myself and that I believed in nothing.

When I used to feel inspired, I would sit at my desk and draw three-panel comics on computer paper using a black ballpoint pen. One of my comics was about a communist named Andrea who lived in a city like Chicago or Philly, and she spent her time plucking blossoming flowers from the gardens of the rich people living in the surrounding suburb. She stole magnolias, roses, and violets and brought them back to her apartment, fitting them in tall emerald vases. Never got caught.

I stood up and walked to the other side of the rooftop, started to run, and then I jumped into the large blue pool in my next door neighbor's backyard. Sprays of water splashed up as I sank into the chilly deep end. I looked around and found that there was a deflated volleyball sitting on the bottom of the pool. I spread my arms out and kicked my feet, swimming towards the volleyball. I grabbed it and swam back up to the surface. The air was warm and humid when I stuck my head out of the cold water.

As I crawled out of the pool with the volleyball under my arm, I wondered when the Phuongs, my neighbors, were coming back from their vacation. I was house-sitting for them while they took a backpacking trip across Vietnam and Cambodia, and they'd been gone for a week already. And today was when they'd come back, but I just didn't know what time. They were Vietnamese American too, so I presumed that was why they had selected me to house-sit. They had a fluency in speaking Vietnamese that I would never be able to match, though I did understand it when they spoke the language, and I could say simple phrases in conversation. They had a lanky black cat with a white belly named Garçon and a lime green gecko named Insurance, and I had been feeding them for the past seven days. For now, Garçon and Insurance were completely reliant on me, and knowing I had this responsibility also made me anxious and neurotic. I'd been paid ninety dollars up front and there was ninety dollars for when the job was finished.

I dried myself off with a raggedy beach towel, put on black sunglasses, and sat in a lawn chair, lighting up a spliff I'd rolled earlier when I'd been concerned. I smoked the spliff and felt the high creeping in on me, my head feeling light, serene, silky. My house and my neighbors' house stood right next to each other, almost too close, my vinyl siding touching their red brick. I heard a meow and glanced behind me and there was Garçon sitting on my shoulder. I stroked his head and breathed in the summer air.

When I walked inside of the house, I was carrying Garçon in one arm and the volleyball in my other. I set the volleyball down on the wooden dining table in the kitchen and then went to the living room to check on Insurance. There was a huge glass container sitting on a long black dresser, filled with smooth stones, batches of golden sand and sediment, a tiny green pond, and a miniature pink house. I looked into the glass container and I couldn't find Insurance. "Fuck me," I said. I took the large plastic lid off the container, reached inside, and lifted the pink house. Insurance slithered out and dipped slowly into the green pond. She winked at me. I waved at Insurance. Then I remembered it was a gecko and geckos didn't blink, or at least that's what the internet told me when I pulled out my phone and searched in Google. I sighed, then laughed, as I walked down the hallway to the kitchen. As I chewed on a strawberry gummy worm, I noticed that the sliding glass door was still open in the family room. The volleyball had sunk into the carpet, a huge gash running through the white foam. I swallowed the gummy worm and felt like I was the worst pet-sitter in the history of pet-sitters. I walked across the family room and stepped out to the concrete patio area. I looked at the pool and there was Garçon resting on the edge of the yellow diving board. "Stay put," I told Garçon, as I circled around the pool heading to him. His back rose up and he flashed his tiny white teeth. I thought he was snarling at me, but instead he was yawning, his eyes sleepy. I walked up the steps of the diving board and walked across it, stretching my hands out.

As I got closer to Garçon, I lunged forward and reached for his legs. But I missed and Garçon scratched my forearm with his paw. Then I tumbled backwards into the pool, splashing into the cold water, feeling like I was everything and nothing. I held my breath and closed my eyes. I saw my comic character Andrea in the water. She was wearing a red swimsuit. She had long black hair draped over her slender shoulders. Green eyes and freckles. She swam over to me and kissed me on the lips, tasting like rust and chemicals. But it also felt blissful, and in the moment I was grateful. I opened my eyes and she was gone, and there I was all alone again.

I lifted myself out of the pool and saw blood leak out of the small cuts in my forearm. I wiped the blood off with the towel as I walked back into the family room. I couldn't believe Garçon had slashed me up, and I'd be lying if I didn't feel betrayed. I swung my foot forward to kick the deflated volleyball and ended up slipping on it. My head hit the floor and everything went black.

When I woke up, Mr. Phuong was standing over me with his hand stuck out. "You okay?" he asked me.

I nodded and grabbed his hand. "I'm alive."

"Where's Garçon? I can't wait to see him," he said, pulling me up to my feet. He looked me up and down. "You look rough, kid. What happened?" He pointed at my forearm.

"Oh, I went for a run and ran into a tree branch."

"Really?"

"Yup."

Mrs. Phuong walked into the family room and smiled at me. "Thanks for house- and pet-sitting, Andrew." She walked over to me and gave me a hug. "Oh," she said, taking a step back. "You're wet."

"I was in the pool earlier. Did a few laps."

"Good exercise, huh?" Mrs. Phuong said.

"The best," I said. She smiled again, but this time it didn't seem authentic. She turned to the side and pointed down the hallway. "Did you take out Insurance and play with her? I didn't see her in the container."

My hands were shaking and I shoved them in my swim trunk pockets. I shook my head and said, "She's probably in the pink house."

"She's not. I checked," Mrs. Phuong said with a frown. "And the container lid was open."

I knew I was going to have to lie again, but I didn't know what to say. And as I opened my mouth to speak, there was Garçon skirting quietly into the family room. He purred, and there was something small and green swinging from his teeth. He was holding Insurance by her tail, and she looked frightened and worn out. Blood dripped onto the carpet.

Mr. Phuong looked at Mrs. Phuong. She looked back at him. And then they both looked at me and started cursing me out in Vietnamese. Mr. Phuong smacked Garçon on the back of his head as Mrs. Phuong started to cry. Garçon spat out Insurance. And she landed on the floor and scrambled out of the family room, past the halfway open glass door, slithering into the backyard. Mrs. Phuong picked up Garçon and yelled at him, and he made a face.

Mr. Phuong rushed outside, stepping onto the patio looking around for Insurance. He looked back at me and told me to get the hell out. I nodded and said sorry in Vietnamese, then sorry in English. Words came out in a jumble. I started to walk out of the family room. Mrs. Phuong was standing in front of the kitchen, bouncing Garçon up and down in her arms and crying. She raised her fist at me and yelled, so I turned around and walked out to the patio and closed the door behind me. Mr. Phuong was searching under the lawn chairs and the lawn table. He checked the tall green trees bordering the pool. And then he marched around the pool, looking into the deep blue water. I inhaled. Exhaled. I told him again that I apologize for screwing things up, and I really was sorry, I really was. Mr. Phuong wasn't listening to me anymore. He sat on the edge of the pool and covered his face with his hands. He was muffling his screams.

As I began to walk out of the backyard, I saw Insurance blending in with a pile of fallen green leaves, then scrambling into the tall stalks of grass. I chased after him as he squirmed deeper into the grass and dirt. He was burrowing into the ground. I got on all fours and reached out with my hand to grab him.

Aberrant Abecedarian

NICOLE TONG

abide by this   patchwork of beginnings the world does not end despite
a cross over the body of the dead   acrostic skeleton of only one bone *A*   in-
adequate   these days I am a lonely mathematician   of anachronistic
aesthetics traveling by ambulance   anything to come to a starting place   un-
afflicted   I can't get to point b   if painted then all gesso &
aggression   all marrow no bone   both the backstory and what lies
ahead
aimless as air   airwaves from home   this office   now a classroom door
ajar   incoming dog begins to gnaw
akin   kindred   as a kid the neighbor's toddler sketches in chalk
aligns her feet to the shapes she's made on the sidewalk
amasses sticks should they need a nest   this ambiguousness does not bother her n
anecdote for anger   but soon   all our annals annotated   as if anxiously
A-1   for the first peak to slow the spread   we wrote our year in
apologies   approaching approbation
a quarantine on display   *come meditate be mindful   catch us on Zoom Happy Ho*
argot for 2020   artlessness aside   I admit I too tossed sourdough starter
assuaged my Catholic beginnings with prayer   asthmatic and afraid   I
atoned the old-fashioned way   each rosary felt like an
audition for what might come next
a verse   averse to verbs   and their tenses this wholly American narrative
awash with empty
axioms   *we're in this together*
ayes have it   this arrowed
azimuth

Swagger and Swish

CEDRIC TILLMAN

The hardest thing
the children have ever had to do
is watch her get dressed,
now that their father

shudders at maleness,
now that her needs
are inexorable,
a shade of skin.

The youngest,
just now into men
and makeup, blooming
with potent imprecision.

At last, that vexing
and obstinate wind
leans a fallacy of orchids
into submission.

No Visible Scars

VENUS THRASH

Not hands clamped around a throat. Liquor
fueled fists crushing the nose. Blackening
an already puffy eye. Not a knee to the gut.
But there is a kind of violence that scars
just the same. Dampens joy. Wounds the spirit.
Burdens the mind. Suffocates the soul. A more
subtle breaking of bones. A barrage of putdowns.
The backhanded compliment designed to degrade.
Withdrawing sex. Rejecting intimacy to hammer
self worth. To starve desire. To punish perceived
wrongs. To recycle pain. To hurt when hurt.

American Progress

VENUS THRASH

Staring at the photos side by side
they could be brothers. Emmett leans
an elbow on a floor model TV in a dress
shirt whiter than anything else in the frame
besides the eyes brimming of so much future.
Babyface Tamir fresh cut and trim heather
gray hoodie bashful grin enhanced by the sun
radiant in a background window bursting light
all around him like a crown. Months after
the images are snapped   one on black
and white film   one by android phone
they'll both be murdered.

Guys Like That

DAVID A. TAYLOR

WESLEY SAT AT THE BAR staring at the thin brown packet propped against a Harp tap. Why did that Petaluma return address look familiar? Sure, he'd lived in Petaluma for a few years as a kid, but it wasn't that. It was the thirtysomething guy in a leather jacket who'd just handed him the packet in the hotel lobby. Could he have been a childhood friend Wesley didn't recognize?

"Do I have to sign for it?" the bartender asked. He side-eyed the package, then Wesley's brown jacket, and raised his eyebrows. "I thought you were off-duty."

Then the name hit Wes: Randy Powers, the dweeb in third grade. Wes felt a twinge of regret recalling how he'd picked on that kid when they were ten. It'd been too easy. No, the guy in the lobby couldn't have been Randy.

Anyway, water under the bridge.

Wes's memories of his childhood were scattered, plumed like a deck of cards. Being in the army, his old man had moved them around everywhere. That was one thing Wes decided early: if and when he had kids, he'd stay put.

He tapped the package on the bar and wondered if it was really as important as R. Powers of Petaluma had claimed or if the guy was just blowing smoke. Could it possibly be the same Powers? Wes replayed the conversation in the hotel lobby. Though it had happened just minutes before, the lobby scene already felt oddly distorted. This Powers guy in the jacket had stood in front of the UPS kiosk gaping, disbelieving the word Closed. How could it be closed for *him?* Was he such an entitled prick? Wes took another sip, decided he couldn't tell. Maybe the dude was okay.

"Another Cuba Libre, chief." Wes tapped the bar. When the bartender returned and placed the glass in front of him, Wes said, "You won't believe this story."

Wes knew this bartender loved a good story, and he would tweak bad stories until they were good. Vegas clientele must give him a lot of material. Sometimes when the TV overhead got unbearable, the bartender would walk over to the jukebox and drown out the news with an old show tune. Then he'd roam the bar in a kind of dance, riffing with his customers.

"Try me," he said, leaning over the bar toward Wes.

Randy Powers considered the Sony convention a small roving city of its own *within* Vegas, tens of thousands of people needing food, shelter, the works. And Randy had the contract for handling Sony's film-editing monster for broadcasters, a car-sized machine that had him running all four days of the convention. It was a good contract and kept his house moving business alive during the winter, and in this economy he wasn't biting any hands. This was his fifth Sony convention. He knew the widths of the dolly to a sixteenth of an inch, the best moment for pulling the truck into the bay, and how long it took to unload, set up and break down. By the last day he was wrung out and jittery — no sleep, no time to eat. That final day blurred with late orders from buyers and local station reps who'd prowled the booths for three days, plus all the chaos of tear-down.

After all that, back in his room he had just enough time to mollify his soon-to-be-ex-wife, Carol, in a call before a bedtime chat with their daughter. As Carol rattled on, he eyed the packet on the bed, the one he thought he'd sent. Carol was deep into the divorce procedure: a household inventory, documentation of his absences, the sit-down with a lawyer. He'd dreaded this, but once they started down that road, Randy knew it was crucial to switch gears. He'd seen it many times: guys getting screwed by staying in husband mode long after the tide had turned. (He'd never thought it would happen with him and Carol!) After talking with a lawyer, he now had to get a signed form and a check out for next-day delivery to avoid giving Carol grounds for slapping him with non-support. Everything through the attorneys! Randy's lawyer had told him he had a good shot at custody of Kira, but that would depend on proving that he was a committed parent. That meant dotting every 'i' in the process. The guy was emphatic.

Randy managed to keep all of this out of his voice in his calls to Kira. But she was five, old enough to hear tension.

"You should see these machines, Kir," Randy said that night. "Twice the size of your room. You could climb in and feel like you were in a big Tamagotchi."

"Daddy," Kira admonished. "Can you *bring* me that Sony?"

"It's too big," he said. "It would have to live in the backyard. And it would get ruined when it rains."

They talked some more and said goodnight. After hanging up, he raced down to the hotel lobby. He'd timed everything too close with his red-eye back to Chicago and hadn't left any margin.

When he got downstairs he saw the darkened UPS kiosk. Of course it was closed! He stood staring at the glass and the deserted counter.

He imagined smashing his forehead against that glass. He'd glimpsed the packet that morning as he walked to the bathroom and stepped into the shower, and still he hadn't handled it. Why not? Normally he made plans and followed them. This practice dated back to third grade and the precision tactics required to avoid the fools at school, at church, at Little League, on the street. Like Wes Johnson, who prowled Sunday school as well as Randy's nightmares back then. Randy never really knew what had started it, he just knew that Wes would suddenly appear at the pool or the bus stop and start hassling him. At the pool, Wes and his buddies took turns dunking him. Hiding behind a tree at the bus stop, Wes lobbed dirt clods which exploded at his feet, making him cough like a little old man.

Randy learned to plan his daily route very, very carefully. Planning was how he'd grown his life.

Randy's worst episode as a father came when Kira ran home crying that she'd been bullied by two kids at school. He'd gone mute with rage. Days later he caught himself driving past the bullies' homes at night like a stalker. Yet he couldn't manage to talk about it with anyone.

Damn! In the hotel he slapped the slick brown packet against his leg and looked around the lobby.

While he stood there, a guy about his age walked up and said, "Is there a problem?"

He was sturdy, a little taller than Randy. He wore a coffee brown jacket, open, and brown pants. Randy had noticed this guy come out of the hotel's bar. He might have weaved a step. The guy's posture stirred some kind of suspicion in the pre-thinking, reptile portion of Randy's brain.

Randy took a breath, then explained: the package, the deadline, this closed UPS kiosk. In his worry, it all tumbled out.

The guy started to laugh. *Fantastic*, Randy thought, *It's near midnight, I'm wasting my time telling this idiot my problems, and he mocks me.* A geyser of rage welled up from his feet. "You think that's funny?" he said.

The man straightened up and tugged at his jacket, actually pointed at his heart. This nut job was crazy, or drunk. He seemed to be itching for a fight. He might get it.

The guy was pointing at a gold and brown shield on his jacket.

"I *work* for UPS," he said. "Problem solved." As he spoke, he *was* swaying a little.

"It really needs to get there tomorrow," Randy said slowly. "Seriously. There's a kid's future hanging on this."

The man in brown placed a hand on his shoulder. "I shit you not," he said. "This will reach its destination faster than if you'd dropped it off this afternoon. You have my word." He looked at the package, seemed to pause.

"You really sure?" Randy said.

"Hell yeah," the man said. The guy looked Randy in the eye as if checking something. Then he handed Randy his card. W.S. Johnson, driver, United Parcel Service.

Thinking back now, Randy didn't know what to make of it. The guy had seemed genuine. At the risk of appearing ungrateful, Randy had repeated that it needed to get there tomorrow, so if Mr. Johnson couldn't do it, he'd better say. The guy waved him off. "Trust me," he'd said. The last Randy saw, Mr. Johnson was headed back into the bar with his packet. He got a bad feeling.

The image of the man disappearing into the bar stayed with Randy. Through the taxi ride to the airport, Randy was sure he'd just made the stupidest decision of his life. He'd panicked and trusted a stranger. The taxi was rushing him to the airport (he still could miss the flight). Why'd he given the packet to a drunk? Laid off, for all Randy knew. Wearing his jacket for a night on the town, hoping to find someone with a uniform fetish. Randy stared at the man's card again. He'd go online as soon as he could. If UPS couldn't track the package, he'd…

A wave of fear surged through the taxi's back seat. How could he have done this? Randy imagined Johnson at a bank counter, still in uniform, endorsing the check with the lawyer's name. He imagined Kira, waving sadly through the back window as Carol pulled away.

The bartender laughed. This one had some possibilities.

"For example," he said, "who's the package addressed to?"

"He *told* me who it was. His lawyer," Wes said. This bartender sometimes didn't listen. They both looked at the address again.

"So," the bartender said, "he said it was about his kid's custody. But do we know that?" He drummed his thumbs on the bar like a soundtrack for an emerging idea.

"I don't know, man," laughed Wes. "I just know that if this *was* the guy, as a kid, he had a stick up his ass. Even as a kid!" He shook his head. "I had no idea. He just looked like an opportunity for a smile."

"I'll wager he's suing to take some kid *away* from their mother. Guys like that don't change, man," the bartender said, shaking his head. "Not really." There were only two other people in the bar, huddled together. The bartender did a little jig over to the jukebox and tapped on its side while he searched for the right song.

"That's bullshit," Wes said. "I mean, *I've* changed a lot just since my twenties."

"You're not that guy," said the bartender, still poring over the song titles. "Dumping his problems on some stranger. For all you know—" He stopped, struck by one of the choices.

Wes glanced at the packet again, inspected the handwriting. He'd dated a girl once who was into analyzing handwriting. Weren't those long diagonals condescending?

"It's probably an eviction notice," the bartender offered. "He's probably evicting some old lady who's fighting for custody of *her* granddaughter. Like that case in Florida?" His finger stopped halfway down the glass. "I don't know. But guys like that don't change. Trust me. Guys like that look all benign when they're helpless in a hotel lobby. It comes out, though."

Wes took a sip, savored the tang of Coke against rum, and considered this. Certainly possible. But screwing over Powers now ran against his sense of who he'd become. Sinatra oozed into "Wee Small Hours."

The thing nagged at Wes as he drove back to his place. He'd paid for his own bullshit youth, but what compensation had he ever gotten for sparing others the consequences of *their* bullshit? Zip. And what price had Randy Powers paid for all the condescending bullshit he'd undoubtedly doled out since third grade?

Wes suddenly saw the pale tile corridor where he was frog-marched to the principal's office. Pulled out of Mrs. Henderson's class and walked down that hallway to sit and wait for the principal, no idea why. And then to hear it was because he had horsed around with Powers at the pool? A couple of dunks and little Randy's overheated imagination. People like Powers left a trail of blindsided interrogations – slighted coworkers, supervisors, wives and exes. And had Powers ever paid a price? Hadn't paid squat, clearly. Powers rode over other people like a monster truck and still looked offended that a UPS desk would close at 9 p.m.

Wes kept coming back to that. It was on his mind when he drifted asleep, the package on the chair across from his bed.

When he woke up, the situation looked different. The world was sunny and new. Why hassle Randy Powers, someone he hadn't thought about in thirty years? Wes didn't have the time or the blood pressure to spare. He threw the envelope in the truck, gave it to Kathy when he reached the front desk and said it was urgent. "Today, okay?" he said.

"Got it," she said. "Oh, there was a voice mail for you. A DC."

A dissatisfied customer? thought Wes. *How the hell—?*

"You want to hear it? It hasn't gone to Relations yet."

"Sure, put it through." Wes sighed and pressed 1, and soon heard Powers' quisling voice: "—You know, maybe he really did send it, and if it gets there tomorrow, then it's all good. But I'm concerned that W.S. Johnson—according to his tag—immediately walked into a bar after he said he'd do his job and get my package to its destination. Please confirm." As Powers gave his phone number, Wes heard airport P.A. announcements in the background.

Wes flashed on an image of Randy Powers as a kid, dripping against the sun-whitened cement of the poolside walkway. Soaked, rubbing his face, ears stuck out at a ridiculous angle. Wes felt again that gut-level response: *Dunk that nerd! Dunk him!* The universe demanded it.

Wes stared out at the parking lot. He fingered his phone, let out a breath through his lips, and tapped in the number Powers had just left in the voice mail.

ScrewNoDaddy

DARLENE TAYLOR

FOUR TAG AND BUMP SHOULDERS as the bus stops; they laugh as school children do on playgrounds. Loud. Throwing their heads back. Bending to their bellies. Fingers pointing at each other, bubble gum sticking to the sidewalk, pigeon droppings on a crumbled napkin and empty French fry cup. The bus door opens, and the littlest pushes to the front. She stumbles toward a seat and then bounces from one row to another. The other three stroll on and peel the straps of their backpacks from their shoulders.

The boy and the two older girls sit across from each other beneath wheelchair stickers and take out their cell phones. The tiny one scoots beside the boy. She sticks a finger in her nose and reaches for the boy, but he blocks her hand from touching his. The youngest, surely not much older than a toddler, taps at the back of the boy's phone case until he turns his back to her.

Heads down, phones in front of their faces, the bigger girls read their screens. One chews a wad of gum. Her ponytail is loose with shorter uneven hairs jabbing the air as if she had finished a fast run. The other pulls her headband to her forehead. They talk among themselves of homework that's too many pages to read and an assignment that's due tomorrow.

How come you don't come out no more?

Can't, she says, chomping on the gum. She rolls her eyes and snaps her fingers at the little one. The little one stands, extends her arms, and balances in the aisle. Her ponytail dips into the hood of her jacket as she raises her eyes to the support rail that is three times her height and far out of reach.

What else you got going on?

A science test on Wednesday. A vocabulary test on Thursday. Arithmetic on Friday, the gum chewer says before snapping her fingers again.

The little one rocks and shakes as if in an aerobic workout. Get over here, the girl says as her cell phone vibrates. The little one waddles until she falls against the bigger girl's knees. The girl doesn't look up from her phone.

I already failed that test. Now I got to read for a multiple choice and fill in the blank quiz too?

You see Pokey?

Her friend shakes her head no and swipes the phone screen. A pink gummy ball covers the front of her mouth. The little one's eyes widen as the bubble gum fills with air until it is the size of an acorn, then a tangerine. She readies a finger to jab, opens her mouth as if she would chomp the bubble. The bus jerks and the girls lurch forward. The orange-sized bubble sags and hangs from the bigger girl's mouth.

He don't come around no more. She pulls the gum from her mouth and rolls it between her fingers.

Mommy, the little one says and plops between the two girls.

Neither looks up.

You going to the dance? the girl asks as she twists her headband.

Mommy is the girl with the spiky edges. She stretches her feet into the aisle and arches so that the back of her head brushes against an oily smear on the window. She pulls a notebook from her backpack and glitter spills on her lap. Damn.

Rain. Rain, says the little one, squiggling and tracing a fingertip in silver sparkles.

I got stuff to do, Mommy says, plucking at a clump of flecks.

You still young. Why you can't have fun?

Who got time for dances? Mommy asks with a side-eye and no interest in an answer. She pulls the little one on her lap, smooths curls at the child's forehead, and pulls the tiny body close. The bus rattles and the two giggle and jitter as if finishing an amusement park ride.

A Where am I? glare locks Mommy's black-black eyes on concert signs posted on a construction fence. What the—? Somebody. Somedumbbody sprayed *ScrewNoDaddy* in blue paint across her mouth. Why somebody do that? she asks and presses the gum under the bus seat. Some dumb boy messing.

That message ain't you, so don't be feeling all sensitive like I know you do.

This morning her face clean with a smile like she just brushed her teeth, Mommy says, then clucks her tongue on the back of her teeth. She raises her hand like students do in class when they have the answer, loops a finger over the yellow cord, and tugs midway, a tired end-of-day stretch. A flat ding like an out-of-tune metal xylophone alerts the driver to stop.

Get your eyes out the phone, time we get off, she says and slides her phone in a pocket. The boy doesn't move fast enough; she kicks his feet with the toe of her Converse sneaker.

Hey, quit, he says and jerks his head up. You play too much.

A sad red brick building stands beyond a bus stop trash bin and a skinny-limbed tree. Three gather backpack straps. The little one reaches out for someone to take her hand. No one takes hold. The bus halts and the four alight, tallest first.

The little one jumps the last step and lands on the sidewalk in a loud thump. One, two, three, she says at the top of her voice. She dashes as children do on playgrounds. Three chase laughing.

The Lesson for Today

ADAM TAVEL

for James

My strings slice finger plaques each time I ache
a chord to show my son he has to press
until the notes ring clear. At ten, it stings
his fingertips, which in a month will slab
with calluses he'll need to riff away
his headphone nights. By then he'll know two frets
by touch, will know that when I sigh and bleed
our lesson ends. Beyond his door I'll rag
my Gibson down and shout above the crunch
to help him find the bridge. But today
we wince in tune and tap our stocking feet
to keep our changes clean. He makes us crank
our knobs to shake the house. We share the curse
to rush the beat that runs inside our hurt.

The Light at the Beginning of the Tunnel

YERMIYAHU AHRON TAUB

I walk down the corridor past a closed door;
light leaks out from beneath.
I speculate about the activities of the person behind it.
Is he listening to music on headphones?
Perhaps Vivaldi. Perhaps heavy metal.
Is he watching television on mute,
the colors from the screen illuminating his night face,
the images dancing over his indifference to
or unawareness of my presence?
Perhaps he's reading *The New Yorker*
or an underground comic.

I follow footsteps with trepidation:
the movement of …
let's call him the man from the bar.
Why am I here? Why did I get into the car? Why tonight?
How did my inexperience become unbearable, repugnant even?
Why didn't I give him my number and meet him
for cappuccino and biscotti at another time, in another place?
Why did I follow him from that watering hole in the wall?
These questions swarm around me unanswered, unanswerable.
And still I move forward, following him,
to the threshold of the sham Eden at corridor's end.

The man from the bar is now above me.
How fine he is, refined even, chiseled in a glow so delicate
he insists it must not be obscured.
The invasion begins without an opening volley.
I beseech, my white flag frantically aflutter.
My cries ricochet off his resolve.
He tells me to shut up, stop struggling.
I obey, float above myself, in the nether region

between witness and onlooker. If I don't ...
He proceeds methodically, relentlessly ...

until suddenly, finally it's over. Or is it?

In the morning,
he returns me to my basement without banter,
deposits me on my doorstep.
Now he knows where I live.
I wonder again about his housemate.
Did he hear? Surely this was not the first time
pleading prospered in that room.
Perhaps I should be fortunate he didn't partake. At least that.
Below ground, I dab in vain at the blood—my virginal secretion—
and entomb myself under covers for days,
under shrouds for decades.

The Rowing Coach

EVA K. SULLIVAN

IT WAS THREE DAYS before the first high school rowing regatta of the season, and March hadn't quite transitioned from lion to lamb. Coach Laurie was using every extra minute of Daylight Savings Time to work the varsity rowers hard. They had just completed a four-minute power piece up the Anacostia River past the Benning Road bridge and were hunched over, breathing hard, and waiting for her to catch up in the motorboat. Budding beech trees, vines, and marsh grasses lined the riverbank. One would never guess this lush greenway was in the heart of Washington, DC.

"Good job," Laurie shouted through the megaphone. "Catch your breath and get some water. We're doing another piece." The inflatable life jacket didn't provide any warmth against the rushing wind as she drove. She always told the kids to dress warmly because it felt ten degrees cooler on the water. She wished she had followed her own advice. Even with two layers under her windbreaker, she was chilled.

In contrast, the kids were stripping down to their performance T-shirts.

What had started as a beautiful, bright afternoon was quickly turning into a blustery evening. The winds cooled the air as the sun grew lower in the sky. If they were going to be back on the docks before dark, they'd have to row full pressure upstream. They could not be late for the bus again or the parents would be all over her.

"Sara, what was your stroke rating?"

The coxswain moved her microphone away from her mouth so that she could shout back to the coach without deafening the girls in the boat, who had speakers under their seats. "We got up to thirty-four strokes per minute," she said. Sara was the most experienced coxswain on the team, and yet she had gotten into the boat wearing shorts. She must have known her legs would soon be covered with a colorful array of discarded jackets from the overheated rowers.

"It looked like you were all together at the catch," said Laurie. "Make sure you square your oars early on the next piece."

The boys' varsity coach had not shown up for practice, which was unlike him. So Coach Laurie was alone on DC's "forgotten river" with both squads: two eight-person rowing shells, each guided by a coxswain barely old enough to drive a car, eighteen teenagers in total. Why had she agreed to this? She knew she could count on Sara and the girls to steer straight and avoid collisions; however, she wasn't as familiar with the boys' crew. She just wanted to get through practice without any disasters, always a possibility with young people whose frontal lobes were still developing.

She checked the line-up list on her clipboard then picked up her megaphone. "Jason, I want you to give the girls a two-boat-length head start, okay?" Jason gave her a thumbs-up signal. There was way too much chatter in the boys' boat, but she ignored it.

The tides and rains had left the water high and flat, near-perfect rowing conditions. Laurie would have loved these conditions when she rowed in college. She had spent so many early mornings pulling an oar through the waters of DC's larger, more turbulent waterway, the Potomac, that rivers were an inseparable part of her psyche. The Anacostia was once considered a polluted, sick, urban dump. But it was now home to turtles, beavers, and bald eagles. These kids didn't know how lucky they were.

As the racing shells moved upstream, Laurie dropped back so that she could follow directly behind the girls and see all eight blades feathering and catching in sync. The boys had passed them, turned at the bend, and were out of sight momentarily.

Laurie was distracted by thoughts of her recent breakup. Her boyfriend wanted to date other people. Why couldn't she accept that? She inhaled a familiar earthy smell that somehow comforted her.

She took a minute to gaze off to her starboard side, where black cormorants perched on the bare tree branches near Kenilworth Aquatic Gardens. Their wings spread out like little Draculas waiting for nightfall. Off to port was the National Arboretum, with its lonely little dock. Normally the river felt alive with rowing teams charging past. This afternoon, the grounds were deserted;

there were no people anywhere. Not even the private school teams were out practicing. *Is it a religious holiday?* Laurie had never been alone on the river, and it made her nervous.

She lifted her sunglasses and could make out a dozen or so geese pecking in the grass, getting ready to settle in for the evening. One always had its neck extended, on the lookout for predators while the others grazed. Her ex used to stand next to her like that at parties. She already missed him and yearned for that lost sense of belonging. A rich honeysuckle smell wafted across the water and mingled with the gasoline fumes of her two-stroke engine.

All of a sudden, a sharp snap caught her attention, immediately followed by the distinctive puttering of her engine shutting off. A whiff of white smoke blew toward her. *Damn!* She coughed. *Did I hit a log?* She glanced up and down the river, secretly hoping... for what? That someone would rescue her? She lifted the outboard motor. A large branch protruded from the propeller. Laurie then rolled up her sleeve and plunged her hand into the frigid water, grabbed hold of the branch and wiggled it loose.

She was so focused on getting the students through practice safely that it never occurred to her what would happen if she herself got stranded. The rowers were nowhere in sight. She swallowed hard to keep down a rising sense of panic.

It took three tries before the engine would start up again.

The boys' Eight was gone. But the girls had stopped their boat near the footbridge just after the river turn. She loved them for that. They would get cold quickly once they quit moving, especially with the wind picking up. As she drew closer, she could hear music coming from the boat. They appeared happy together, oblivious to the anxiety she wore on her face. Nine faces turned toward her as she neared their port oars resting flat on the surface.

"Coach!" Sara shouted—no recognition of the engine difficulty she'd just faced. Adolescent egocentrism was something she had studied in grad school. She often laughed about it with the boys' coach. They were just children. Big, strong children. "Megan's hands are bleeding!" The tall girl in Five Seat held up her raw, red palms.

She was reluctant to do anything that might delay practice.

"I have some tape."

She opened a large duffel bag—the one that contained the required U.S. Rowing safety kit and all the life jackets—and took out a little medical pouch.

"Can you catch it?" she asked. "I can't get any closer."

Laurie stood up in the launch and bent her knees to position her body for a gentle underhand toss. At the exact moment of the throw, her lower leg pushed against the tiller—which had repositioned itself due to the wind—and she fell over backwards into the bottom of the motorboat. Her prescription sunglasses fell from the top of her head into the water behind her.

"Coach!" all the girls shouted at once. Her motor launch was heading toward the fragile shell with surprising speed. Even with the engine in neutral, it was moving faster than she expected. If she hit them at this rate, her sharp bow would crack their boat in two and she'd have to rescue nine girls out of the water. That was not going to happen on her watch.

"Push me away with your oars!"

Laurie stood up, the seat of her pants wet from stagnant, cold water on the bottom of the boat. She grabbed the tiller to correct the steering, but the metal prow of her launch had already made contact with the girls' blades. The Eight was getting blown closer to the shoreline, where submerged branches could break the skeg, the small keel that balanced the narrow shell. Or worse—put a hole in their hull.

"Bow and Three Seat, *row!*" She had no time to pick up her megaphone. "Stroke Seat, hold water!"

A gust of wind blew them into the shallows. Starboard oars struck against the mud of the riverbank, and the bow was inches from getting wedged under a fallen tree. Sara was yelling through her coxbox, but Laurie couldn't hear the words. She needed to grab her megaphone, but it had rolled out of reach. Or she could back her motorboat away from the Eight and give them room to maneuver. If she didn't act fast, this could be disastrous.

Reflexively, Laurie grabbed the edge of the oar closest to her. With her other hand, she shifted into reverse, then turned the tiller to face into the wind.

Except instead of reversing, the motorboat lurched forward. Without her glasses she had not been able to read the gearshift.

A metal-on-metal clash filled the air. Then a sickening crack, as the rigger behind Five Seat pulled off the fiberglass gunwhale. Laurie's chest heaved with the horror of what she had done. She couldn't see clearly, but her ears understood the damage. She switched hands on the tiller and backed up too quickly. A little cry escaped her mouth.

She focused intensely on the girls, a bitter taste in her mouth. *Whose brain had been hijacked?!* She was glad the boys' coach wasn't around to witness that! She reached for her megaphone and guided them to the middle of the river. Megan, the tall girl in Five Seat, had pushed Laurie away and was now turned around, holding the oar handle of the girl behind her. She was calmly coaching her teammate, showing astonishing maturity. Megan's rapid response held the boat steady in a way that she hadn't, an unexpected role reversal.

Laurie had never administered first aid on the river. She reached for the medical kit, took a deep breath, then motored slowly with great precision toward the rowing shell. Megan helped the injured girl into the motorboat, unscrewed the oarlock, and lifted her oar into the motorboat. Her leg was bleeding, hopefully a superficial wound.

Sara's soothing voice blared out from under the seat, "We got this!"

The way the girls took care of each other gave her a surge of pride.

Challenging situations reveal character, her ex once said, *not change character. You never know who will rise to the occasion until you're in a predicament.*

In the motorboat, Laurie quickly treated the girl's scrape. It might need stitches. She felt a tightness in her chest, as if she had just finished a 2K race.

The boys' Eight was undoubtedly heading back to the dock. But with a damaged shell and whitecaps forming on the river, how could she leave the girls? She'd probably have to go to the emergency room.

She cursed the boys' coach silently.

The girls' extraordinary reactions made her decision clear. "Sara, row steady pressure all the way back. I'll meet you on the dock!" she shouted. "You can do this!"

As Laurie approached the waterfront park, she could make out a lone figure standing on the dock. The boys' Eight was just landing.

She motored carefully into her slot, quickly tied up, and assisted the injured girl out. She rushed to the low dock to help the boys.

The boys' rowing coach had already guided the boys in, asked the bus driver to wait, and now he stood on the lookout for her and the girls.

Laurie felt so relieved that she choked back tears.

At that moment she knew that they should never have broken up.

Waffle House

DANIELLE STONEHIRSCH

When the Waffle House closes, you know it's time to get the fuck out of town.

Waffle Houses never close. Even FEMA recognizes that shit. It's called the Waffle House Index, and they have actually used it to determine how seriously we ought to be taking hurricanes. Just last year, I was driving home in the snow, regretting ignoring the warnings. I was peering through the windshield, squinty eyed, wipers going at full power, crawling along thinking: Lord, here we are in my time of need. Please show yourself and light the way to Heaven. As I wondered how on Earth I was going to recognize my exit through the blinding white, there was the light of the Waffle House right before Exit 3, guiding the way home. I passed it slowly, so slowly I could count the people sitting in the grimy booths, backs pressed to the cracking red plastic. I knew I was going to make it. The Waffle House is America's guide, the light in the storm. The Waffle House is also my employer, although for $8.46 an hour, I don't feel a huge sense of loyalty. I also work at Target for $8.50, but that extra four cents they give me over minimum wage buys them exactly four extra cents worth of my gratitude and we all know that in America today, four cents isn't worth shit. Before my Grandnana passed she told me stories about penny candies and nickel stores, but all I see these days are $5 Dollar Generals along the highway and I have to work a full hour to afford a bag of Hershey Kisses.

For $8.46 an hour, six hours a day, five days a week, I get to clean literal shit off the countertops and the bathroom floors so I can head to Target and clean literal shit off their counters and floors so I can keep the lights on another week for the cats and for Jill. Jill used to clean literal shit off the floors and counters of a Denny's before a drunk guy in the parking lot bashed her head against the brick wall so hard she was out for a week and never quite made it all the way back. Tuesdays though, Tuesdays I leave the Waffle House at 6:00 p.m. and head home to a bottle of wine that tastes like cans, and Jill and I watch movies until midnight, the same ones we watched when we were kids because we still have Mom's old VHS player and the tapes we cleaned out of her basement before we had to sell the house. Today is Tuesday, and as I mop the bathroom where some kid who was too short for the toilet tried to pee, I just keep reminding myself: Today is Tuesday. Jill and I will watch *Escape From Witch Mountain, Clueless, The Fox and the Hound.* When we watch, she'll remember before, and cleaning shit today will feel less shitty. There's crud all over the countertop by 5:00, and I have to lean in with the rag, pressing and scraping my fingernails through the dirty cloth. These people are animals, most of them tourists in for a week of Disney magic and pampering, and while everyone should get a vacation now and again, it's no reason to treat those of us who live here like the trash I know they call us when they head back to New York or Chicago. Or when they sit here thinking trash can't hear them, in between demanding more coffee, more sugar, more syrup.

A family sits in the corner booth, both kids wearing the Mickey Mouse ears and flinging syrup from their forks onto the napkin holders and the ketchup bottle. The parents ignore them, poring over a brochure or a map, figuring out how to make their next day perfect. Isabel in the kitchen shouts at me that the order for booth six is ready, and I drop the rag and grab the plates on the counter. I can't carry them all at once, so I'll have to come back for the side of bacon. It's a short distance to booth six, but there's an obstacle course of syrup and a fork on the floor, a chair pulled out too far from the table on my right, and a wet spot at the end where Daisy finished cleaning ketchup just ten minutes earlier. I make it through like a fucking gazelle and lay the plates down. The booth seats two boys and two girls who I can only assume are their dates. They think they're hot shit with their class rings and their uneven bangs, and one of them has his hand in his girl's lap right in her crotch, as if I can't see. Before I've finished setting out the last one, the other one, left arm over his girl's shoulder like he actually gets that he's in public, leans forward.

"Where's my fucking bacon?" he says, spit flying onto the table hash browns.

"I'm getting it now," I tell him.

"I ordered bacon," he says, but he's looking at his friends now. "You better not charge me for bacon you never brought."

"I didn't forget the bacon. I'm going back to get it."

"You lying to me about bacon? Like this job is so hard? You fuck up just bringing the food people ordered to the people or ordered it?" He laughs, and they laugh with him. Short, breathless giggles that set my teeth grinding as I walk away. It's hardly the worst I've heard around here, and it's Tuesday. It's Tuesday. I call Isabel over from the other end of the counter and hold up the bacon.

"Booth six doesn't want this anymore."

She rolls her eyes and moves it off the counter. We're supposed to throw that stuff away, but not all of us have much waiting at home, so untouched rejected plates are Waffle House gold. I turn my back to the counter and lean against a stool, smug in petty revenge. These kids think they're going so much further than me, but the truth is there's no way I don't come across at least one of them, three years from now, pushing a mop ahead of me at the Target, cleaning up shit while I stock the shelves.

By the time I'm finished imagining barking orders at the floppy banged mop pushers, I have only thirty minutes left on my shift. I'm leaning against the counter as Isabel is telling me a long story about her ex-husband's new girlfriend and how she let Isabel's daughter walk to the corner store alone at night. A man walks in wearing a coat, which I notice right away because it's a hundred fucking degrees out. His hair is long and a little gray and a little stringy. The coat is making him look bigger than he is. His sneakers look like they were made for a kid, with a bright red stripe across the middle and puffed-up heels. He looks right and left as he comes through the door, and my stomach drops before I understand why. It's not a far distance from the door to the counter, and when he's halfway, he reaches into the bulky coat and pulls out a gun. He looks at me, and I realize I've been standing in front of the cash register. Isabel takes a step back, towards the grill. At first, we're the only people who realize what's happening, but then there's a gasp as the mother of the Mickey Mouse-eared kids looks up and grabs them, one in each hand. A couple at a nearby table looks up at the sound and freezes in their seats. The other customers swivel at once, until only booth six is still talking. The man turns toward them, shaking the gun by his side, and yells, "Cell phones down, hands on the table."

"What the fuck?" says the bacon kid, and his eyes widen when he sees the gun. His hands fly into the air.

"I said on the table," the man repeats, and after a moment, the boy's hands slam down, knocking over the napkin holder and spilling his drink. I am inching away from the cash register. I can feel the cold metal against my back, pressing on my spine as I slide, and all I can focus on is the strong smell of old coffee grounds and burning oil. I don't even see the other boy move, but I see the man lift the gun and level it at the booth.

"You don't need to shoot anyone," I say, and it comes out even and normal, like I meant to say it, which I didn't. He turns, and I can see his eyes. Cloudy blue. Lined and puckered in the corners from too much sun. He levels the gun at me. I wonder if he registers the color of my eyes. Jill is in the closet in the hall now, on her knees, looking through the boxes of video tapes to pick out two so that we're ready when I get home. The cats love getting into the boxes, so at least one of them will be prowling behind her, jumping over her arms, getting his claws caught in the cardboard. When she's made her choices, she'll take her two tapes and sit in the brown armchair where the cats will take their napping places on either side of her. She'll wait for me to come home.

The kids in booth six are all looking at me now, frightened. So is everyone else. "What's in the cash register?" he asks.

"Money," I say.

He shakes the gun at me. "How much money?" His hand is shaking. The gun trembles back and forth, and I worry he'll set it off by accident. It's his first time, maybe. Or he's high. How much money does he think there is in a Waffle House cash register? If he shoots me, will the Waffle House close? Does a dead waitress count on the emergency scale? Or will they make Isabel mop up the blood, wipe down the grill, and set up a sign where I fell that says "Caution— Wet?" Who will think I'm worth closing for? No one, not even Isabel, who needs the $8.46 to keep part custody of her daughter. Rob will be here at 6:00 to take the next shift, and they'll ask Daisy to cover for me tomorrow morning. They'll rewrite the schedule for the rest of the week, and families will keep stopping in on their way to and from the parks, and soon they won't remember who cleaned the bathrooms or carried the bacon. I'm not a hurricane or a tornado or a pandemic. Just a forty-year-old waitress who lives for Tuesday nights. No one wants to lose money over me. "Open it," he tells me when I don't answer.

I turn around slowly. The most I've ever seen in the register at one time was three hundred. What makes this guy willing to shoot someone for a few hundred bucks? I hope I am worth more to the Lord than that. I open it and feel sick. There's about sixty in there. I pull out all the bills and hold them up. He just stares at me, and I know he hasn't thought the whole thing through, how he's going to get the money from me without getting close, where he's going to go next. If he doesn't shoot me, I'll get the fuck out of town. Jill and I can pack what we've got in the van and drive until we hit Georgia. I'll do something better. I'll be better. We'll be better. It's not too late yet. The man pointing the gun looks older and grayer by the second. I say it out loud. "It's not too late." I hope he believes it.

Meditation for My Country

ROSE SOLARI

From another angle, that row

of tumbled bricks becomes

a mountain range, and then that range

a chain of cloud on cloud that now

is water's wind-blown climb and fall.

You know these figures — reeds

blown clean for music-making,

every breath and finger pressing toward

the whole. What if we could live this

always, our notes in sweet

cooperation, clustered like stars

in our linked and brimming hands.

Coronavirus

MYRA SKLAREW

Single strand of RNA
wrapped in your protein coat,

a halo of spikes ready
to bind to an unsuspecting cell.

Some say you are not alive!
Yet you with your secret partner,

Sars-CoV-2 who picks the locks
on the protein spikes,

and then invites you
to enter the cell

of your choice, all the while
turning off its immune system

so you may safely enter,
head for its nucleus, create

infinite copies of yourself,
and calmly disrupt the world!

There Must Be a Gate

LAURA SHOVAN

Where there is a wall
there must be a gate,
a way to enter the garden
on the other side.

Birds need no permission
to migrate overhead.
Moles tunnel the earth
to get through.

For them, brick and concrete
are inconsequential,
barbed wire,
a human concern.

We must pass through the gap —
if one exists — wingless,
clawless, on the same two feet
that carried us days

and miles to reach this wall.
Identity vouchers
and proof
of public education

are sewn into our pockets.
There must be a gate,
we tell ourselves.
We have seen this wall before.

Mendacity

LAURA SHOVAN

The business of being dishonest
helps protect the worldview
of American shareholders.

Let's dump the word "citizens" –
Sad! Untrue! It's safer, not dishonest
to call America a business.

Not a democracy, but messiah
of capitalism to the world.
And it's safer to replace the media –

So unhelpful! Totally unfair! –
with advertisers. They offer us
protections much safer than "free speech."

What's free in life? Nothing.
You're already paying
more than your fair share.

A Real Woman

KIM SHEGOG

MAMA SAID, "Pants? Over my dead body," and we have one of those already, so it'll have to be the black denim dress.

****

She should've told me how much more there was to it than "sperm meets egg" like they taught us in health class. It all seemed so scientific—based on time and situation. Something I could control by not thinking about the probability at all.

Bridget was a mess, and she'd run Daddy off by then. Not that I expected him to talk about sex. God, he could hardly open his mouth to mention the weather. She gets half the blame. For letting me go when she should've said no and for making me feel like I couldn't come to her after. Like I'd be the disappointment, the embarrassment—even when there was Bridget. Any other time, she would've laughed in my face if I'd come begging to go to the movies with a senior. Not this time. She waved me away. *Dallas* was on.

I'd called him back and told him I could go. Heard him grinning through the phone, I swear. I was one of the cool girls, riding in his dad's Camaro with the windows rolled down. Even though both fenders were rusted, I was proud when strangers looked over at us at stoplights.

He bought us a popcorn tub, which wasn't cheap, and we split an orange drink. When I took my first sip after him, a tingle ran all over my body. He was sharing himself with me. He took my hand from my lap and placed it in his, smoothing the skin with his fingertips. When he reached over and unbuttoned my jeans, I was surprised but not afraid. Even when he climbed on top of me with his jeans lowered to his thighs, I felt warm and ready.

For a while, I was exactly what somebody wanted.

After the credits ended and the screen went black, somebody cut on the light, and he jumped off me, pulling up his jeans and yelling at me to hurry. He dragged me by the arm through the fire exit door. No alarm sounded like I thought it would.

He didn't open the car door for me like he did when he picked me up, and the radio was blaring country music so loud I couldn't say anything if I'd wanted to. When we pulled in the driveway, he reached into the back seat without looking, grabbed a sweatshirt and handed it to me.

"Root for the Mountaineers," he said. "I'm headed to Appalachian next year."

I only had half the money for it. I took the rest from Bridget. She was back in the psych hospital, so she wouldn't be needing it anytime soon. Christy's cousin told me about the place and gave me a ride. I wore the sweatshirt he gave me and jean shorts. There was a blue vase with fake yellow flowers on a coffee table in the waiting room. The man, a doctor I guess, said everything went fine.

****

I cup my hand over a full belly—full of stillness and silence. A little sadness, but not regret. Never regret.

I think this fits okay. It's snug in the hips, but it's better than nothing. Really, I do mean nothing. It's the only dress I own. What do I even have this for anyway? There—last snap of the band and hair is up. It's too warm to leave it down, and it's the last thing I want to have to fight today.

I grab my makeup pouch from the dresser and rest it against my knee on the bed. Where is that tube of mascara? I dump the contents on the comforter. Here it is. Now the compact mirror. A little black cement on these lashes, and I'm all set. Maybe a finishing touch of nude lip-gloss.

Graduation. That's it. All the girls were supposed to wear white knee-length dresses, but I couldn't find one I liked. I tried. Went to two different stores. The fit they threw about that at the lineup. Mama too, once she found out. But like I asked them, what difference did it make? The gown covered it up, so who'd know?

Brown heels. Oh, Mama'll love this. Shoes don't match the dress, heaven forbid! Doesn't she realize it's Dad's funeral, not a pageant?

I jam the pile of shoes on the closet floor, poking them this way and that, but the door still doesn't want to close. It's the corner of the egg crate that's caught. On the top is the scarf box. Haven't looked at this in a while.

Granny Roxie's gift for my thirteenth birthday. It was folded into a perfect triangle so one full blackbird showed when I peeled open the tissue paper. I'd groaned at the time, telling her I'd never wear a scarf—it wasn't me. She'd insisted I'd grow into it.

There were many times I sat with it on my bedroom floor, smoothing it to its full square and tracing my index finger over each silhouette. Beak to black breast to claw. Their midair flight across a sky of white silk.

If I could just get this tied on right, it'd help. I fold and crease, unfold and smooth, and bring it around my neck. The mirror's reversals offer little help. No bird has a head, now only feet show—a bead of sweat drops into a crease. What the hell am I doing? I pull the silk tight, enjoying the punishment for my own inadequacy, then release. I reach for the yellow beaded necklace bought with my own money for some forgotten event. At least it hides the red streak.

I fold the scarf to fit its box, aiming to expose a blackbird inside a crisp triangle, but fail—again.

I'll never be that kind of woman.

Rent

GREGG SHAPIRO

The check is always, usually, sometimes, often
late. Either the money's there or it's not. The amount
fluctuates depending on what came in, what went
out. Debt and death, fees and penalties, are certainties,
shelter less so. Dare I ask the daddy long legs, the pill
bugs, the silverfish and swarming ants, the centipedes
and palmetto bugs, to pay their share? What about

the pale chameleon corpses that litter the ground
beneath the desk of this office where the blinds
are drawn from dawn to dark. Do they have rights?
Do I? Renting time in this broken body, tenant and
landlord, I can't tear myself away, rent the fabric
like a dazed mourner. Here until the next pogrom
or plague, rate increase or revolution.

Kingman Lake

COURTNEY L. SEXTON

Honey
suckle through the fence
teeth on this island
in the middle
of a city caught

in the middle of a century
they built Heritage,

dredged the banks
of the Anacostia
and poured
silt like through a sieve
until you couldn't see the river
anymore but around it—

They said you sit there now and stay,
Nacotchtank no more; They said,
"It's for the children…"

…then let the sludge carnival roll slowly

down the backside of the divide.

Now, four black legs dangle from the dock
without touching
the water; under the surface
an extra limb could grow
or one never form, just be
the trace of an isotopic glow.

So what asylum, what refuge there
is in abandonment

only the heron could say – great blue-grey –
but he won't look you in the eyes
as he wades, knee-deep

through hypoxia
toward Buzzard's Point.

Southern Pine Beetle

COURTNEY L. SEXTON

I.

There are rhythms that we do
and do not
feel—

You look up at the trees and fail
to consider the layers breathing
beneath the bark. Consider
the breath, once your own, returning.

II.

My fingernails are my father's, picked
but not bitten
down to the quick
rough and white
with jagged cuticles, an insult
to the beds they rest in.

I watch him absently scratch
at the brown cluster of cells that could be
a tiny beetle
on this cheek, his fingernail (my fingernail)
digging out a cancer.

III.

The Southern Pine Beetle moved
north because one day it realized it could stand
the seismic shift of air.

Now there are scores boring
into the pitch of my pines,
boring past their first line

of defense. The trees are not going down
without a fight, but last fall
we had to fell at least five—
the beetles having invaded, teethed past
the hard, dried cells and even the running sap
meant to drown them.

They call enzymatically
to each other, reach out across the island, to the mainland—
Larvae multiply, break out.
Needles brown, skin sloughs
away even as the turn-
coats within send the signal – reverse S.O.S. – for more
sweet cancers to arrive,
more beetles to bore into us,
the trees, I mean.

IV.
My mother comes to visit
and when she leaves
I am left with her
skin. I brush it
into a little pile on my jewelry stand;
wipe it gently off of the toilet seat;
let it blow
out of the car window.

I have vacuumed three times since
she's gone and I still can't bring myself
to siphon the traces she shed
Because after all won't I wish some day
that I had kept it, her
skin?

Blind

LEONA SEVICK

Once, my brother and I thought she was just
a terrible driver. Too many times to count,
she'd drive us home from town in darkness,
headlights off though street lamps were scarce
and anyway didn't reach as far as we needed
them to. She drove slowly enough, her hands
at 9 and 3 like they used to teach us. Our road,
twisted and dangerous, was darker still, and when
one of us would shout *turn on your headlights!*
she'd reach for the nob slowly, shake her head
while we howled. I wonder now if she did it
on purpose, chose not to see the factory where
she worked, the rusted cars stacked on cinder
blocks, the broken down houses lining the road.

Brothers

ADAM SCHWARTZ

MY BROTHER'S GIRLFRIEND, Jannie, had had enough—of my brother, Oren; of their bickering; of a country that elected Trump; maybe of me.

On her last night, she took a taxi to my apartment. She came in, and we hugged. "You don't have to do this," I said.

I wanted her to say *you're better than Oren—more patient, more loving, more understanding, more willing to be interested in others*, but she just massaged her forehead, closed her eyes and said, "I need a break." Tears welled. "Just everything."

Brothers are supposed to look out for each other, be there for each other. I tried on a look of tender, melting concern, then pressed her roughly against the door, dropped down, and shoved my face under her miniskirt.

Afterwards, the two of us collapsed on the foyer floor, she said, "This is why I can't stay here."

For a while we were quiet, staring at the plaster medallions on the ceiling.

Then she was up, collecting her clothes, getting herself together. "I feel better now," she said. "Clearer."

"Why?"

She held a butterfly hair clip in her teeth and lifted her hair in the hall mirror. "Oh, I don't know," she said. "Oren's such an asshole."

Let her go. Before you destroy everything.

"Why don't you stay tonight?" I asked. "Collect your thoughts. I'll get us a hotel. Something nice, where we can relax."

"Relax?" Her face jutted forward.

My dress corduroys and boxers were still down at my ankles. I tugged them up and fastened my belt.

"Do you know what I have, Lyle?" She counted Xanax inside a prescription vial.

I was quiet.

"I have the gift of no illusions," she said.

"I don't know what that means."

She held the vial up to the light, sifting it. "You've been amazing. And I feel terrible for tangling you in all this," she said, "but right now, I'll just take a ride to the airport."

The next day, Oren, crazy and helpless, had crossed the Atlantic, chasing her.

* * *

A month later, I met Oren at the airport. I was terrified that he'd discovered what Jannie and I had done. I love my brother. And for this reason, I could never tell him.

Oren was not alone. He had with him a war veteran who'd been a gunner in Korea. Pink-fleshed and bull-necked, Phig was an enormous man with an enormous head and a spatula pug nose. They'd met at a hotel bar on the Rue de Trevise and had been travelling and drinking for weeks. During this bender, I received slurry accounts from Ciens, where Phig and Oren tobbaganed, stayed in an Alpine windmill and evidently had too much paté, and from Cote D'Azur, where they irritated several Lerin monks and Phig developed a nasty case of zosters, making it necessary to stop from time to time so Oren could rub the old man's feet.

By the time they limped into SFO, Oren and Phig were like two old lovers making allowances for one another's foibles. We drove north up the bay, the three of us, to Lucky Hou's, one of those places in Chinatown where withered ducks hang upside down in the window and pine crates of live chickens are stacked on the sidewalk.

In a deserted dining lounge, we were shown to our red vinyl booth. The air was heavy and warm. We had not said a lot to each other yet. My brother can be cagey. Maybe he was just biding time—savoring his advantage—before pouncing on my betrayal.

Oren ordered a duck for himself. Hunched over the fatty bird, he picked at it with primitive gusto. I pushed aside my snow peas and watched him. My brother and I share the same dark Mediterranean skin and sad dark eyes and nearly identical chins: a deep crescent groove arcing over a meaty bulb of flesh. I saw then that a thick cut was healing under Oren's chin.

"That's gonna scar," I said, touching my own chin.

"So you're a doctor now?" A forkful of chow fun dangled before his mouth. "You don't look good."

He sized me up with benevolent patience. "A couple nights with him"—his head cocked toward Phig—"and you'd look worse. Now don't spoil my duck."

Phig shrugged, a spare rib bone between his teeth.

"You should have seen Phig that first night." Oren threw an arm around Phig and rocked him back and forth. "This guy actually thought I was French." He buried his glee in Phig's shoulder.

"You must be pretty good to catch his French," I said to Phig.

"What's that?" Phig screwed up his face.

"My brother's French," I said. "It's not good."

He ran his tongue through the narrows of his gums, crowding me with his hulking silence. "I like the sound."

The senile brute was dangerous. I saw that now.

Oren took a napkin across his mouth, composing himself. "Thanks for picking us up."

"It's nothing," I said.

"The customs agents took some strawberry preserves and a marzipan princess I had for you," Oren said.

"I don't agree with that at all," Phig remarked to no one in particular.

"Agree with what?" I asked.

"Homeland security," Oren said bitterly. "The big guy asks questions. The other one helps himself to my personal effects. It's all in plain sight. It's like a big joke."

"Right in your face." Phig wagged his head sadly. "There's the price of admission."

"They seized your jam?" I asked.

"They didn't *seize* anything," Oren said. "They *stole*. They took something that wasn't theirs. That's what stealing is."

My heart thumped in my chest, and I put down my fork. "What're you saying?"

"What do you mean, *what am I saying*?"

"I don't know what you're talking about."

"You don't?" Oren asked.

"No," I said. "I don't."

His face broke into a wide smile. "How can you not get it, Lyle? I told you. It's these bastards in TSA. They've got their dark blazers and crackling wands touching things they're not supposed to touch, and every so often they pluck some poor rube out of line and help themselves to whatever."

I tried to make myself laugh. "You have trouble with people in uniforms. It's always something. You bring this on yourself."

"You're not following here, pal," Phig scolded. He hunched forward and began chopping one hand into the palm of the other. "*Vigilance. Preparedness. Cooperation.* The whole time, this is how they're talking. *No more secrets. The crisis isn't over.*"

"What he says—exactly how it happened," Oren said. "There's nothing you can do."

"It's like, what's the word?"—Phig snapped his thick fingers—"a violation of trust."

"Yes," Oren chimed in, "a violation of trust."

"There's laws about that," Phig warned.

"Securing the homeland," Oren said disgustedly. "What a joke."

The waiter came and cleared the plates. The old man's feet had begun to swell. When Oren reached under the table, Phig's knees shied up and he pawed my brother away. Still stooped, Oren shot Phig a mothering glare, and I watched Phig sigh and swivel his broad hips girlishly, lifting his feet. He settled his weight, getting comfortable, while my brother cradled in his lap the giant's fleshy yellow heels. He began to work.

"Should I go?" I asked.

"His feet get puffy," Oren snapped. "Is that a problem for you?"

I looked away.

Phig's head was tipped back, grey eyes vanishing into his skull somewhere. An odd purposefulness absorbed Oren. As he pressed the flat of his hand into Phig's tender arch or raked his knuckles across the meaty soles, I imagined the old man's feet drawing the color away from Oren's face.

"You look just like when you got the bends scuba diving in Mexico," I said. "All pale and sickly."

"That was terrible," Oren said. "Everything was fizzing."

"You couldn't get your air."

"We should go to Mexico," Oren said, tending to Phig's ankle. "Sun. Tequila. Muchachas."

"You'll be on the can all night," Phig mumbled drowsily.

"We're not going anywhere, Oren," I said.

"I promise not to keep you up. I know how you don't like that," Oren said.

"What is there ever to say that can't wait till morning?"

"Is it the money?" Oren asked. "If it's about moolah, that's not a problem."

"It's not the money."

"You teach seventh graders all day," he said. "How can it not be about money?" From a glassy brokerage suite above the bay, my brother had fattened on millennial boom. He liked throwing money around.

"Look, Oren, you're not yourself right now. You look like one of these guys that hangs around gas stations."

"Do yourself a favor: square up with the tax man before you start making comparisons."

"You would bring that up."

"Well, it's true."

"It's irrelevant," I said.

"Auditors call your house."

"Alright, alright." I looked around the room. "Keep your voice down."

"Phig doesn't care if you cheat the government."

But Phig was out, more or less. Tentative, delirious moans wheezed from his lips as Oren kneaded one arch and then the other.

We were quiet for a time.

"You know, over there, I really thought Jannie and me had a chance," Oren said. "Like we'd figured it out, maybe, once and for all. We were forgiving the crap out of each other. I could see how it could all be different—you know, better."

"Jannie made you crazy, Oren. Remember?"

"Sure, after a while, I was ready for the hemlock, no question. Who wouldn't have been? All the animals she brought in the house? *Five* cats?" He raised a hand, fingers spidering out. "Five of them. You can't even tell people this. It's something you gotta hide. But it wasn't just the cats. It was everything. The hot yoga, the fake meat—she'd go ripshit on people for wearing leather." He paused reflectively. "Remember that crazy Gila monster? She went to Baja to clear her head and came back with an iguana. Can you imagine?"

"I remember him. Miguel was his name. She worried his neck was stiff."

"She'd let him out when clients visited. Investors become very skittish, very risk-averse, with an iguana in the room. She knew this. I had my worst year ever when we had Miguel."

"You two fought over that," I said, thinking back.

"All I said was 'that thing oughta be repatriated.' That's it. Do you have any idea how long those reptiles live?"

"No."

"Decades. That bastard Miguel could've ruined me."

Phig shifted his weight, eyes still shuttered. "Maybe she was going through the change," he said.

"She's thirty-three!" Oren cried out.

Phig's lips pursed apologetically.

We were quiet for a time, Oren tenderly pressing his thumbs into Phig's sole. Then he said, "Let me ask you something."

I looked up. "Sure thing, Oren."

"Now I want you to be honest with me."

"Go ahead," I said.

He studied my eyes. "I want you to tell me if you slept with her."

I repeated the words dumbly. "Slept with her."

"Yes."

"C'mon, Oren."

"It's a fair question."

"You're shittin' me, right?" I demanded, arranging my features in a display of incredulity.

"It doesn't really matter at this point, Lyle. After all, Jannie's gone now— permanently estranged."

"You don't know that."

"I do. She's not coming back."

I poured myself some water from the pitcher.

"I know you never meant to hurt me, Lyle. I know that."

"Don't get carried away."

"Might feel good to clear your conscience. Go ahead. It's alright. Say it already."

"This is stupid, Oren."

"Make you a deal. You tell me, and I'll take you to Mexico."

"He already told you he ain't going," Phig mumbled.

"Phig's right," I said. "I'm not going."

"You didn't think I loved her enough," Oren said.

"Did you?" I asked.

"What kind of question is that?"

"You brought it up."

"What about when you convinced her to join Torah study?" Oren pressed on.

"You think I'd use sacred writings to get your girlfriend in bed?"

"It was you two and that ditzy chick with the pretty mouth," Oren said. "You weren't studying the Torah."

"I tried. We—it was a phase. What's the matter with you?"

"She said you guys had some really good talks."

"Talks, Oren. Talks."

He teethed his lower lip.

"Think what you want," I said.

A long silence came over us. Oren brushed rice grains from the table. I turned my face toward the window, and as I watched my reflection, I could feel my brother's eyes—restless, full of questions—settle on me.

* * *

I remember when Oren and I were young and our father would sit us down in the screened-in porch and read to us. Robert Frost and Kenneth Fearing, realists who would caution us against hubris and a fallen world. Our father was a remote man, but he loved us and he always impressed on us that the world could be bitterly unfair. I think he felt that he was arming us. I would lose myself in the comforting rhythms of my father's voice, and I would try to trace the arc of our futures and imagine what life would be like for Oren and me. We were young, but even then I sensed the vicissitudes awaiting us: formative disappointments from which we would be expected to learn, some deepening understanding of ourselves that we'd turn to good account, friendships that I naively imagined would keep forever, establishing careers that our parents would approve of, our emergence into a world where all things would be possible, the women we would meet, women we'd love.

* * *

In the months that followed, Oren began to put his life back together. He found new clients, replacing the few he'd lost while away. Oren is good at what he does, and the market continued to be kind to him. He brooded less and again found new ways to absorb himself: taking on a new golf swing, working with various fertilizers to create the greenest lawn on the planet, and with the aid of Eharmony and Match, dating wildly. Sometimes, Oren would call me, upset over Jannie. But this happened less and less. Phig had long since returned home, back east to Philadelphia, and though he'd gotten over the zosters, the old man's health suffered in other ways.

At night I walk among the people of the Mission, angling up through the sloping neighborhoods. The night air brings the ocean with it. Across the water, the starry eyes of the East Bay gather themselves before me. I stand for a time, feeling the wind rise off the water, trying to think of something else, anything, because everywhere I am reminded of her.

A Blaze of Stars

PATRICIA SCHULTHEIS

A FRIGID SATURDAY, and since lunch, Robert has been sorting through document boxes. He's trying to organize the archives of Burnside, the old mill town where he and Lalita have lived for thirty some years.

The afternoon has begun to wear thin when he hears china rattling. She's bringing him atonement chai. For months, his wife has found small ways to apologize for reneging on their agreement to retire together. He probably should have known that she'd keep working. Ever since he met her at Oxford, she's carried a terror of pennilessness like a turtle carries its shell. But now, holding the tea tray and wearing one of his old NASA sweatshirts, she looks relaxed, toasty, almost content. He smiles.

She sets the tea tray on a box of ledgers detailing the yards of woolen goods the Burnside Company sold to the Union Army. After handing him a cup, she begins shifting through old photos of the mill workers' houses: narrow, stone cottages without central heating or indoor plumbing. Amenities like those came decades later, after the Depression bankrupted the mill, and developers bought everything—the mill, the houses, the school, the store—and transformed a dismal enclave on the western edge of Baltimore into a quaint, Williamsburg-like village replete with shutters, picket fences, and brick walks.

"I know exactly where this one was taken!" She hands him a picture of a dozen young women in crisp shirtwaists and long skirts. "By the little stone cottage near the pond. That IRS guy lived there. A woman just bought it. She works for some NGO."

Robert studies the picture. It had to have been taken on a Sunday. The Burnside workday ran from seven in the morning to five in the evening, except for Saturdays, when it ended at one. Which left the women an afternoon to wash and iron their shirtwaists and maybe take a bath. Yet, here they stand, looking as if they'll burst into a fit of giggles at any minute.

"They're probably Scottish," he says. "Mills recruited from Scotland because they needed weavers skilled in working with wool."

He hands the picture back, and her phone beeps. She goes into the hall to take the call, then comes back. "I have to go in."

Robert knows better than to ask her why. She can't say. She works for the National Security Agency.

After she leaves, he washes the cups. On the kitchen windowsill, a statue of Shiva dances, and behind it stars are popping out across the cloudless sky. He checks an app on his phone, bundles himself into layers of down and wool, and grabs his binoculars.

Outside, Burnside looks abandoned. The only neighbor he sees is the stone cottage's new owner, who's hoisting a suitcase into her car. As she drives past, Robert recognizes that hyperfocus of someone needing to catch a flight. All those years checking tracking stations for NASA. All those flights.

The old mill pond offers the best vantage point for stargazing; few trees obstruct the view of the horizon. He focuses his binoculars on the northwest sky, then lowers them. The sky's so clear, he doesn't need any help to see a diamond-bright object traveling like an errant but friendly star across the dark expanse. The International Space Station, the object of his NASA years, and yes, he must admit, the object of his devotion. He watches until it disappears.

He stands alone by the pond where a grist mill first stood. And then a woolen mill. Step by step, from the grinding stone, to the looms, to three people circling the Earth for the sole purpose of discovery. Progress has been made. He has to believe that.

He walks home up the street, where, in a few months, his Burnside neighbors will celebrate the Fourth of July. He waits for Lalita, and when she's back, he'll gather her to him because, whether by chance or fate, they found each other.

What a wonder—that he, Robert Radowski, from Youngstown, Ohio, whose mother had checked groceries at the A&P and whose father had delivered mail, and whose love of mathematics eventually earned him a Rhodes Scholarship to Oxford, where, one night in a pub, he met a woman who grew up in Manchester after her parents had fled India, and whose prickly personality has never ceased to fascinate him. And that they can lie secure in each other's warmth, in this place built of stone and sweat by anonymous laborers who maybe on cold, cloudless nights just like this one, climbed beneath coverlets warmed by their own beloved, and who, before they lowered their lids, happened to look out the window and see a vision to carry into their dreams: a blaze of stars dancing across a midnight blue expanse of space.

Little White Lies

KIM ROBERTS

There's a whole generation of American Jewish men
named Stanley and Irving. My grandfather's
generation. Ironically, their parents

chose those names to sound American,
by which they meant more patrician,
more Christian. They wanted their sons—

often the first in their families born
on American soil—to fit in, to have
better chances. But as soon as the Christian families

understood the subterfuge, they jumped ship—
and those names quickly turned
from gentile to Jewish. Stanley sounds

like an adverb, and Irving like a gerund.
Where have you been? Oh, I was just out irving.
What would the verb *to irve* mean? It's like the inside

of a swerve, so I'd guess it means to prevaricate. As in,
thinking Jews could be just like them,
as in, by changing a name we could become invisible.

Jewfish

KIM ROBERTS

Epinephelus itajara

Collecting old debts
    is called "chasing the eagle."

Americans are either rogues
    or dupes. As I will never belong

to the former, I must work hard
    not to increase the latter.

Statistically, we're more likely to be bitten
    by a New Yorker than a shark.

In 2001, the American Fisheries Society
    changed the name from jewfish

to goliath grouper. There was a movement
    to change Jew's harp back

to its medieval European name, trump.
    Well: that failed.

Walt Whitman wrote, *the hands of the sisters*
    Death and Night incessantly, softly

wash again and ever again, this soil'd world.
    This is the night we have earned.

Only the Knife Knows the Heart of a Pumpkin

COLLEEN KEARNEY RICH

THE PUMPKIN was perfect. A Cinderella pumpkin, her daughter called it, and they all had to agree. It did resemble the carriage from the Disney movie. But it was hectic those weeks before Halloween with William's big project going off the rails at work and the lice outbreak at the school. Costumes were thrown together after a quick trip to the party store. Then there was the parade in the neighborhood to get ready for, and Lisa found herself tossing that cottony cobweb stuff onto the shrubs and leaving the decorations as that. The pumpkins they bought sat on the front porch until her son insisted they carve one. In a rush, they chose his pumpkin to carve because it was shaped like Frankenstein's head and easy to put a face on. The boy was finally content that the holiday was progressing as necessary, and Lisa managed to keep the seeds from the garbage. After they walked the neighborhood and the kids surveyed their loot, Lisa popped the pumpkin seeds into the oven and turned them into a snack. The Cinderella pumpkin sat on the porch long after Frankenstein caved in and was dumped in the compost. Lisa wouldn't let Cinderella be composted. The seeds, she said in protest. She could still roast the seeds. Then they had to make plans for Thanksgiving. Were they really going to travel again? William moved Cinderella to beside the compost pile. Lisa had forgotten all about the pumpkin until she saw it one morning while making breakfast. Day after day she watched it through the kitchen window, in rain, in frost, in snow, in the slanted winter light. Not even the squirrels wanted Cinderella. Some mornings the sun hit the pumpkin just right, and it looked brand-new, fresh. But it couldn't be, right?

One morning Lisa discovered the pumpkin had deflated in the night, as if some-one let the air out of it. It's time, William told her. She knew he was right but missed that orange face.

The Longest Baptism

TAYLOR RAMAGE

STAY WITH ME. Breathe slowly. This is the longest baptism, and our fingertips nearly break the surface. You've just opened your eyes to the stinging, but I've been here for ages. It's time for you to know these waters.

First, the hulls of massive ships glided above like swarms of beetles, blocking the blurry sun. Across, then back, then across again. The temporary night they made in their passage was peppered with muted splashes, disturbances in the water's flowing silence. In the distance, you could see the bodies sinking with the weight of their fall until the water pushed them up into resurrection. Motionless, bloated, but not destined for where those ships docked.

Then, boots splashed on missions from bank to bank–young men who held these truths to be self-evident: that *they* were created equal. But there was so much blood as the generations sought freedom by a different definition. If you pay attention, you can still see the ripples skating across the surface.

New feet crushed those who had known each rock beneath the surface since the beginning of time. Ever expanding, their footprints scarred the Earth. The stretching towers and the sickening waste came quickly, but so did the bridges that echoed with marches. I saw every color through my wavy, weary lens, first black and brown, then the rainbow that boldly flooded the streets. The rains muffled their cries and carried the dyes bleeding from their flags back here. Sometimes, you'll see the remains float by–a scrap of quilted fabric with a dearly beloved's name and the short years they swam among us before the illness came, or a piece of an outfit discarded for being an abomination adorning the wrong body.

I know. Until now, you didn't realize the depths of these waters or feel them rising. Stay with me. Breathe easily.

Some *do* go down to the river to pray. They submerge as one thing and rise as another, electrified. On those days, this place isn't as murky. I see how light their forms are in the water, so much uncontrollable dancing with the pull of gravity eased. Their movement is a sermon of being dead, then alive, and I start believing again in that first gasp after breaking the surface.

Holes

KIRSTEN PORTER

I.

My cousin knew her for nine months inside of her and two weeks out. She chose the name Olivia and waited until the baby was strong enough to endure the surgery. She knew the odds. Each day she held Olivia she told her, *Please stay here with me. Keep breathing. I can't let you go.* But the baby was too delicate and the surgery failed, and the hole in her heart could not be fixed.

In the afternoon shadows, she held her. She told Olivia she had changed her mind. She whispered to her, *If you need to leave, if you're in too much pain, it's okay now. You can go.*

II.

In a hospital room, the sun slides in sideways through the blinds. My cousin sits in a metal chair and holds my hand. Inside the room, we listen to the IV drip and the staccato register of half a dozen patients' hearts being monitored at the nurse's station outside the door.

My cousin waits until she thinks I have fallen asleep. She leans in close to me and whispers, *If you need to leave, if you're in too much pain, it's okay now.*

Then she is gone.

III.

The phone is ringing from the inside of the house. I push through the door and grab the receiver on the sixth ring. *Hello?* It is my mother. She hasn't seen me in a while, am I feeling okay, am I taking my medicine, how is the weather? I say, *Mom, we live twenty minutes apart. The weather is the same—rain.* I do not tell her that I am short of breath again, that I'm dreaming about my cousin and Olivia, that there are holes in my roof. My mother tells me she means to call more, wants to say sorry for…I hear the familiar punching of her keyboard. I have taken up too much of her time. *Mom,* I tell her, *it's okay now. You can go.*

When I fall asleep that night, it is to the whisper of the rain spilling into my pots and pans.

Admit This to No One

LESLIE PIETRZYK

PRE-EVENING WAS THE PREFERRED TIME for this particular walk, tracing the dozen or so long blocks of Pennsylvania Avenue amidst a liquid glow of pinks and blues as the day's light settled and slipped down into darkness. The between was where he felt comfortable, neither light nor dark, neither right nor wrong, neither Democrat nor Republican. It goes without saying that he would admit this to no one, least of all to himself. But he had been this way always, drawn to the middle, understanding that the world, that all of life, was middle more than edges.

The avenue was congested: heaving Metrobuses groaning across multiple lanes; commuters whizzing home like silver balls lighting pinball machines; cars and bikes dodging and careening in tandem; the criss-cross of pedestrians texting their tardiness and tales of office woe. Only he was calm. Only he was serene, strolling the broad sidewalks as if they unfurled for him.

Like a king on promenade is how he pictured himself, a king strolling to his castle, the image in his mind. A homecoming after negotiating a treaty with the pesky French; or the Knights of the Round Table scattered, left behind, and he, the last warrior, returning from war. Odysseus. If only he were here on a horse, he thought, he dared to think. Camelot hovered like a mist in the back of his mind: *Camelot.*

Traffic lights scarcely interrupted his flow.

No one recognized him, not the commuters, not the haggard five-museums-in-five-hours tourists, not the Asian vendors hawking T-shirts off their boxy white trucks. A homeless man or two spun for a second look, but that was all, was, perhaps, coincidence. He was anonymous, tap-tapping in his Crockett & Jones shoes, handmade for him in England, his head filled with…well, nothing beyond a pleasant sense of undisturbed satisfaction.

The light moved swiftly, coming early in the winter. He had to leave his office by 4:30 to arrive at 1600 at the precise moment. There was urgency to this quest, to the way he called to his staffers that he was headed "out" for "a bit" and they understood not to ask where or why, not to ask anything.

Most assumed a love affair of some type, a tryst: woman, man, boy, girl, girls, women, men, boys. "Nothing would surprise me," some of the staffers sniffed, but this, actually, would surprise them, his love affair with the falling light, with this place, with this lost and dead dream, a thing that once was. Many staffers were too fresh, too certain of themselves to fathom this journey. Others were, he thought, when he thought at all of this team of people who worked for him, who ran his life, who ran him, these others—and maybe most—were too programmed, lacking any wilderness in their souls. He wouldn't be quoted saying this, ever, but in his deepest heart, he knew that his secret, what kept him going, was that tiny bit of wilderness still alive in his soul.

It was fashionable to bemoan the closure of Pennsylvania Avenue, a consequence of everlasting threat of terrorists—but he liked being suddenly dropped out of city streets, finding Lafayette Park and its kooks to his right, joggers lacing their way through the block with grim determination, and to his left, coming upon the tourists gape-mouthed and slow-moving like fish cluttering a cold aquarium, Secret Service and stiff-backed cops, the black bars of the iron fence, and now a new and irritating safety fence creating a new perimeter, and encompassing all this: a certain unique glow. The day's last gleams receding into unknown depths, streetlights flickering to bright life, the tourists tilting their phones and iPads into shimmering rectangles trying to capture it all, their faces slack with awe—"there it is," they murmur—gawking as if the President might pop outside to toss a football or fire up a grill, as if the President might be ordinary— and the godlike silvery-white glow of the building itself, a beckoning, like yearning in a dream, the thing or the essence of the thing he had chased his entire life, what he had sacrificed for, before he was conscious of what sacrifice or pursuit truly meant.

The thing he would never have.

He was not a king returning to a castle nor a king battling for a castle. Camelot would forever belong to someone else. He was only a man standing on the outside, looking in. This is who he had been from the very beginning. Not that he understood this. Not that he would admit it to himself if he had.

Whiskey

PATRIC PEPPER

Some people will look at all the bottles and think & talk & think & talk—about the bottles. Some don't talk at all or think at all. Some do nothing at all—the shot stands short before them. Some people lecture their friends on the proper protocols of drink. On the past & future of whiskey. Claim to educate.

Some recall their bottles of yore: That time in the forest. That time of naked heart. No shot glass. Just the bottle passed & tipped to lips. Some proffer "wisdom." *Cheap whiskey: Better than good beer.*

Look at all the bottles . . .

You and I are not of these people. We're new school & old school. Youthful. Elderly. Vigorous. Full of aches. I tell them, *Fill the glass to the brim.* And when they don't, you command—*To the brim.* We're of another constellation. Of now—no past & no future. Let's take the bottle. Uncap it. Pour. Knock back our shots—fire and all. Say, *Yes . . . Look at all the bottles.*

The News of the Day

LINDA PASTAN

The green earth
is spinning
out of control.

The politicians fly
through closed windows,
breaking the glass,

and doctors are wringing
their hands, entangled
in stethoscopes.

Green raindrops are only
dollar bills.
The children, wide eyed,

lurk under their desks,
and writers complain
that their pens have run out of ink.

Policemen write their tickets
for a thousand abandoned cars.
Slow down.

Like a bellows, breathe
the air in and out. But wait!
The air too is dangerous.

Essays in Idleness

ERIC PANKEY

Essay in Idleness 114

A month (or is it two?) into the pandemic, one day is not the same as the next, but the distinction between them is quite subtle: the five minutes of bright sun yesterday between cloudburst, the sudden racket of the crows' call and response. Neighbors, who have politely ignored one another for years, have taken to waving, to acknowledge at last something shared, even if it is a predicament. We smile behind our masks, exaggerate our gestures so as to be understood at a safe distance. *Look,* we seem to say, *we are alike—alive, that is.*

Essay in Idleness 122

One surrenders and is thus rendered. One cannot unbraid the wick's sooty ends. One draws the dream of the wolves, but then remembers only the drawing and not the dream. One attributes the whispered *shush* to the crescent moon. One builds the walls solid and only later cuts out the door and windows. One kindles the fragile laurel twigs with pitch. To end the initiation (or is it *irritation*?), one admits that the Tao cannot be conveyed by either words or silences. One unties the bride's hair. One continues in a single direction that cannot be reversed. One recalls, as if it were a single hour, cedars in snow and the damp heat beneath a carnival tent. One follows an igneous river to Pluto's dusky domain. One courts discord and is shortchanged. The moment is ephemeral, yet one is always *in* it.

Fractured Ghazal for Baltimore

KATHLEEN O'TOOLE

From a great distance, I grieve my city in flames.
Angry crowds like an oil spill, igniting. Pity and blame

surge as the CNN clips reprise a burning, turning police car.
Predictable reactions – the camera's capacity to shame.

And so, nuance is lost, other narratives, buried.
In this new crucible, intensity's the game.

Before, civil rights pastors, union stewards and housewives
fought to reclaim these blocks, their city of no fame.

Now, with "riot" the lead, Freddie Gray's shadow
grows, glows to an icon's immensity. His name

chanted and wailed. I echo the lament, as new voices
demand a stake, to move beyond the gritty freeze-frame.

Soil

MAURICIO NOVOA

Mami's dreams of becoming
a teacher stopped at the tip
of the corn husk her family
grew, not to sell and profit,
but feed themselves. Abuelito Julio
buried his children's livelihood
in the dirt as Mami learned to make atole
for her siblings while Abuelo and Abuelita Elena
massaged the earth fertilized only by
hunger, so they had to leave La Union.

Papi told me to help Abuelita
Ruth with the backyard
garden, tomates y jalapeños 2 less
things we need to buy at Glenmont Shoppers,
and I said fuck you to
the dirt in my nails as I pulled every friend's
house I don't get to go to that summer
out of the spider's homes that make me
jump back when I find them. From what I gather,
Abuela didn't grow much in San Salvador,
but sold pupusas in the battlefields, where even
their god's chosen mouth piece became food
for the ground.

I loathed the garden until nothing grew
from it anymore, until too many weeds
and grass sprouted that it was useless to dig
my hands in to cleanse it. Until 25 years passed
before I asked Mami what she wanted of her life,
and her dreams were unearthed over atole.

You had asked when I drifted so far away.
You had asked why I didn't turn towards you.

GODDONNY NORMIL

I've been searching for that boy, once so firmly tethered. The boy
      who faced you in the dark that night, and whispered you his life story
      kissed you softly over and over and over
                           until you opened for him
The boy who tore out his beating, beaten, damaged heart and handed it to you;
      dripping of blood and sadness.
The boy who wrote odes to your thighs and poured libations to the curves of
      your perfect breasts.
The teary-eyed boy with the aura of sadness that you plucked from the sinking
      quicksand of his life.
I called you Redeemer… I called you Savior.
      Tonight, I will meet you in the dark again. I will talk to you instead of a
      god that never speaks to me.
I will swear to never revisit what was done in pain.
      Never re-read what was scribbled through tears.
           Never re-hear what was uttered through gritted teeth.

face to face

JEAN NORDHAUS

In the House of Zoom, we sit
each at our window, gazing out

like days on an advent calendar
from a study, a living room, a den

into the common. Some have given thought
to the mise en scène, arranging

the art on the wall, objects and books
on the shelf. I enjoy the display,

but what grips me most is the glimpse
into the rooms beyond, a bathrobe hung

on the back of a door, a hanging pot
in the kitchen just over

your shoulder, the bottom step
of a flight of stairs I could climb

to a place that is hidden.
Imagination helps, but who

can truly grasp the mystery
of another's life? Summer is coming.

Now we see through a glass darkly
images of trouble and smoke

as we wait in our separate rooms
in the one human house.

South Loudoun Street, After Midnight, Tonight

SEAN MURPHY

Competing scents settle for a stalemate—undecided
about what's happening and what already happened.

Old mothers wearing slippers in the summer with
cigarettes like extra limbs, expunging stale smoke
into dying air already appropriate for a screenplay.

Scattered trash defiant and strewn across lawns,
no longer useful indoors but neither noteworthy
nor consigned to the recycling bin just yet.

Warped wood embarrassed by itself, unable to keep up
appearances: it broils during the day and at night the rot
soaks in, settling like caked make-up on an ancient face.

Invisible men search out invisible women while invisible cats
stalk invisible prey beneath fraying clotheslines burdened by
half-soaked bedsheets, waiting for either rain or an intervention.

Street soldiers without homes patrol the sum total of places
they're neither welcomed nor noticed, mutely content allowing
their minds to pull strings as part of a play that writes itself.

Veterans of the alleys and shadows amble or else wheel
themselves in and out of corners, their hearts preserving
what their memories can no longer make any sense of.

Businesses out of business for lack of business insist
it's nobody's business, and the dead animals that keep
other things alive wonder if their sacrifice is in vain.

Nothing to see, nothing to sell, nothing to steal, nowhere else
to go: if this pavement could talk it would and it does—but
it'll take a few news cycles before we know what it's saying.

Streetlights tired of pleading the fifth simply refuse to
shine, and let things unfold the way they do in the wild.

What Is Beautiful to You Is Not Beautiful to Us

BY JENNY MOORE

2020

The child's brow is furrowed, his scowl pronounced.

"You can have one more marshmallow before bath time," the mother says.

"Just two," he says firmly, with surety. More, more, always pushing for more.

She gives him two. She tells herself she is choosing not to fight this battle. Preserving her resources for when she really needs it—bedtime, or toilet training.

Exhaustion has set in, as it does by this time every evening. He wants what he wants when he wants it. It does not make sense to him that it cannot always be delivered in seconds. Some of his protests are brief; others are prolonged attacks, calling on her—*Mommy*—repeatedly, his howling both accusatory and wounded, incapable of understanding her point of view or rationale.

6020

Excavational evidence at the site suggests that at the dawn of the third millennium, American civilization routinely undermined half its population, as did other civilizations across Earth. Those whose bodily apparatuses were capable of growing and birthing children were devalued. The cause for this curious behavior appears to have had no other grounds than biological difference. This group was not the only one constricted and disempowered on the basis of external characteristics. TRAPPIST-1d scholars agree that the practice was one factor in the planet's long-term failure to thrive.

2020

Fifteen minutes before bedtime starts. Going outside is risky, because he might get absorbed and then fight the transition back inside. But she can't stand another moment inside, cycling through the same toys, trying to keep him from growing bored and begging for the phone and its limitless attractions.

Outside he finds his bucket and shovel, amenable dirt. He grins, and the sun shines. All is forgotten but his innocence, his helplessness, his joy in small things. His focus on the present. Really, he can't help his tempestuousness—it's a sign of growth. His passion for marshmallows is adorable.

"Look, Mommy," he says with reverence. He's holding a dead cricket. He wants to show her things that amaze him, that he is proud of.

"Yeah, that's a bug. It's sleeping."

He tilts his head, his eyes fluttering. Miming sleep.

"That's right."

He lifts the bug to his mouth, pretending to eat it, waiting for her reaction. He experiments, using her as a mirror.

"We don't eat bugs. Yuck."

He flings it away from himself.

His impressionability, equally endearing and alarming. He is a vacuum, sucking up everything he hears and sees, then processing it through his incomplete brain.

What he hears and sees is almost entirely up to her. No pressure.

6020

Recovered texts from Earth suggest that the disempowered habitually performed the majority of the work of domestic life, often with little external compensation. Such labor included caretaking of the extremely young and old; educating children; cleaning; and the majority of all work engaging the emotional realm. The premise that the most appropriate use of emotions needed to be grounded in domestic activities illustrates the limitations of this planet's civilizations. These flawed assumptions acted as a major fulcrum in the eventual uprising.

2020

"It's time to work on being patient," she says when the toddler demands the red duck, the only one of his many bath toys not already in the bathtub.

"I being patient," he says doubtfully, tears still streaking his face.

"It's hard sometimes." Yes it is.

This is a stage, one that will end, like all the ones before. Nursing, teething, sleep problems. He will develop, learn, understand rational thought. Remember things and retain information. Be less impatient, less impulsive.

At least that's what the books say.

She does see glimmers, now and then, of increasing cognition.

He tells her he understands the rules. No hitting. No throwing food. No biting. Now, when he does those things, he looks at her knowing what he's done.

"Don't say no," he says before beginning an activity he very much wants to do, anticipating an interruption midway. Trying to establish safe conditions in advance like a miniature OSHA rep.

Sometimes when she does not deliver the requested number of marshmallows, or any marshmallows at all, he accepts it without complaint. As if he expected as much and is accepting her limits. His expression says *Yeah, okay. Worth a try.* She admires both the acceptance and the trying. She wants him to take chances, see what he can get, push against limits. She wants to see spirited, cunning, resourceful, imaginative.

Where do her responsibilities end? Keep him safe. Feed and clothe him. Teach him skills—chewing food, saying thank you, not flinging forks everywhere. Where to pee. But there's all the rest too. They say the first seven years are the most important in a child's life for brain function. If she's doing it wrong she's already down three years.

6020

The capacities for diminishment of the disempowered were ruthless. Apparatuses were objectified and then controlled. Violations of the apparatuses were minimized, ignored, or denied. In an example of the planet's capacity for peculiarity, this portion of the population was elevated for precisely the same distinctions that also marked them for inferior treatment and labor. Those deemed maximally appealing were termed "beautiful." Apparatuses were fetishized at very early ages and throughout their early mature stages. Those measured as "beautiful" were able to exercise some power, though it was often temporary. With further maturation, nearly all were treated by societal mechanisms as invisible or dispensable.

Numerous texts report that a small number among this population did receive positions of significant power, even in some nonemotional regions of nondomestic labor. Many claims of empowerment were made as a result, but later scholars agreed that the system effectively widened the borders of its containment rather than dissolved them.

2020

"I pooping," he announces as she tucks him into bed.

"Let's go to the bathroom." She screams inwardly. She is desperate to think adult thoughts.

"I not want to."

This stage certainly can't last long. She has to see him through or he will be sent home from preschool (if preschool even begins). And if he gets sent home from preschool, he will miss crucial days of early education. Missed preschool could make him less prepared for kindergarten. He might read more slowly and struggle to catch up while the others are building on their solid foundations. There won't be time to stop class for his needs. If any learning disability emerges, a growth stage missed, it may go unnoticed, and the chance for early intervention will be lost. In any case he won't excel, which might make him a target. He will not be picked for games or parties. He'll find violent video games and disturbing subreddits and fail to understand the value of becoming a truly thoughtful caring being. He will be incapable of rationality. Fairness. Humility. Complexity.

Whatever goes wrong, someone will blame her.

6020

The short lifespans and mutations of the bodily apparatuses on Earth created many problems among the species. Along with the challenges already noted, sometimes the apparatuses malfunctioned, trapping an active brain in an undeveloped body, or an undeveloped brain in an active body. In many cases these members of the population were also disempowered, but for a few notable exceptions.

One conspicuous example is from the latter half of the Dictator Age. Texts repeatedly discuss a leader who demonstrated stunted maturation consistent with what was normally observed in a much younger apparatus, such as incomplete speech, oscillating moods, injudicious decision-making, struggle to contemplate, and immature processing of inputs. It intrigues TRAPPIST-1d scholars that this leader described the displayed qualities of temperament as "controlled" and "beautiful."

2020

She sits on the couch in sweatpants, sipping a beer. She wants to turn to herself, but the sight of him asleep, cherubic, recharging, developing before her eyes, is almost more than she can bear. Her daily life is ridiculous, but her love is uncontainable. One day she will have to let him loose.

May he be neither bullied nor a bully.

May he make his own bed and do his own dishes and laundry.

May he be safe.

May his partners be beautiful in more than one way.

May he be kind.

May he understand and embrace emotions.

May he be intelligent.

May he not be the man women warn each other about.

May he never stop striving to see and make more good.

May he be funny.

May he be honest.

May he never experience systemic disempowerment.

May he never contribute to systemic disempowerment.

May his masculinity not be toxic.

May he always love his mother.

May he show his love by both words and deeds.

May he survive in this world.

6020

Research during excavation suggests that this leader's overt endorsement and intensification of the disempowerment mechanisms in American civilization led to widespread erosion of previously acceptable societal norms and did more to accelerate the pace of the uprising than any other member of the species. Unless more information surfaces, the explanation for the elevation of a leader of this caliber will remain one of the impenetrable curiosities in our scholarship of the entrance to the third millennium.

2020

At 4:55 a.m. he is standing by her bed. "Daytime," he says brightly.

"It's not time to wake up yet. Time to go back to bed."

"Play toys, Mommy."

His voice is fully awake. There will be no resumption of sleep for several hours.

"Come lie down with me."

"Play toys, Mommy," he says, louder.

She waits a few seconds, trying to reach back toward sleep. "Go find a toy."

Too soon, he is back with a dump truck and clambers up.

He says her name until she opens her eyes. He inserts a finger into a nostril and watches her.

"We don't put our fingers in our nose."

"*I* wanna do it," he says.

She sits up. She has no choice but to be awake. A toddler runs her world.

Botones

OFELIA MONTELONGO

Month 1 – Mes 1

You hate these days of the month when everything hurts so bad that the buttons sewed on your back want to scream wide open. You scratch them a little bit and put some lotion on them. But today, they are feisty. They want to rip open your body.

You look at your leg and turn on the volume of button number one.

"You're not sleeping well," button one says. "You need to exercise more and eat better."

You roll your eyes even if the buttons can't see your face. You turn it off and turn on the volume of button number two.

"Yesterday I dreamt we went out for a ride," button two says. "We saw the world again."

"You know we can't," you respond to button two. Button two understands what you are feeling. Button one, all it does is tell you things you don't want to hear. You wish you could just rip it out from your body, but if you do, the flesh hole won't last. And you can't get out to get a new on, because of the pandemic. So, you wait and let the buttons you like—buttons two and three—talk to each other. You know how lonely it gets back there, so you let them talk to each other about what your organs say in the darkness inside of your body.

Outside your window, snow fills the streets, ignoring people unable to breathe indoors. Your quesadillas taste like Clorox, sometimes like Purell. You smile at your quesadillas because you know your botones like them. You want to make them happy.

You scratch the three of them again, feeling their mirror-like material, and ask yourself why they can't sleep at night. You look through the window and wonder if your buttons are the only ones rebelling. Are your neighbors also screaming inside themselves?

Month 2 – Mes 2

The cherry blossoms are blooming outside, and you wish you could tell them to wait and stop falling from their trees. The wind still blows even if you can't feel it from your window.

You are not sure if you are getting used to being inside or if your buttons finally decided to give you a break. They are not itchy or demanding to go outside. They sing sometimes. One day they even asked you to dance with them. It is a bit harder to find them with your fingers and scratch them because the fat of your back has extended. You scratch them because you want to and not because they are demanding you to do so. You understand their views are limited. You understand they need you. You can't tell them your throat is itchy because they will want you to stop going to the balcony for fresh air.

On the balcony, they feel happy because they can see other people passing by. Other face-masked women stroll by with their back-buttons out in the air; some women's buttons are made of wood, some others made of plastic. Where are they going? You wonder. Are they saving people? Are they essential? You wish you could be essential and save people, but your life is in front of a computer. You get back in as soon as you hear the police or the sirens of the ambulances. You don't want your botones to see or hear that.

You let button one speak again. "You think I can't tell you what I think because I can't say it aloud, but I have my ways," it says. The voice of button one has changed. You are not sure if it's mad because you prefer button two and three. You feel mistrust in its tone. It thinks that because it was your firstborn button, it deserves all the attention. You turn it off again.

At the end of month two, button number four appears near my cadera. Was four always there? Why did it show up just like that? Button four doesn't understand my accent. When I say something, it understands something else. You think it is mocking you. How can four not understand you if it is part of you? You then realize something has changed outside too, not only on your body. People are marching outside protesting. They need haircuts. They want freedom. You ask your buttons if your hair is bothering them. They say no. "It tickles sometimes," button three says. "Pero no importa," it repeats. You love button three; it code-switches like you.

Month 3- Mes 3

Mes number three starts like nothing special. Button one says it needs to be cleaned often. Cállate, you tell it, but you know it doesn't understand you. A whiff of freshly baked bread fills you every time you go out to the balcony. Sometimes it's combined with marijuana and sometimes with spicy meat. You let your buttons listen to Instagram lives with you. They ask you questions. Button two asks why people are crying. Button three asks when are we buying a coronavirus-shaped piñata?

It's Memorial Day, and you think it will be like any other day, but you are wrong. You don't know what the word looting means, so you Google it. Across the country, people are breaking windows and entering stores. Across the world people are marching with their facemasks on, demanding justice and the end of racism. You want to go outside for the first time. You want to break that tempered glass and chant again and again. You want to fight for justice for George Floyd. But you have a secret only your buttons and you know, so you can't get out. You can't even tell it out loud. You want to pause the world like you pause your Netflix shows. You want to stop the video as you do in Zoom calls. Even before the pandemic, you were tethered to your home.

Smoke is rising outside your window. Gunshots fly around among birds and penetrate bodies chanting.

Washington, D.C. is on fire, and you're still indoors, wondering if there will be month four. You want to break free. The four sewed buttons scream wide open and release themselves from your flesh, drilling you. Your back has now four holes bleeding. You want to stop your organs from leaving your body, trying to sew back your buttons. But your buttons are dying outside of you, so you put on your facemask and leave your apartment for the first time in months. You join the crowd, and your blood interweaves with their blood. Your buttons are seeing the world again, this time on the palm of your hand. Your only hope is for a bullet to finish sewing your back; a bullet to close your bleeding; to finish with your pain.

Good People

CARON GARCIA MARTINEZ

I HEARD THE NEWS when Hal and some of the guys on the early shift came to the site that day in April, irritable, griping about being hungry. "What gives?" I asked.

"The Coffee Spot was closed. No sign or anything—deserted parking lot."

"Man, I had already tasted those eggs rancheros, Lupe's strong brew, but… windows and doors shut up tight. We knocked, looked for Luis's truck, but no one opened the doors."

No sooner did my cell phone start ringing. I answered to Marsha's voice. "Toby? Holy crap, Toby. They've arrested Luis. Lupe's here frantic with the kids."

"What the hell's goin' on?" I said. "Hal is just in here telling me no lights on, no cars, no food at the Spot. Luis didn't even stop servin' all the times Lupe was in labor."

"I don't know details. She's crying and said '*la migra*' grabbed him in the driveway early this morning. None of the kids went to school. What is '*la migra*'?"

"Make her breakfast. Calm her down. Put the TV on for the kids. I'll see what I can find out."

At Goody's Bar, guys trailed in one by one for a lunchtime beer and the latest. Many of us stared at the table and shook our heads.

"Sure don't seem fair," said Brice.

"But why? What'd he do?" I said.

"I heard an old drug charge, 30, 35 years ago—somethin' with marijuana. In Texas," Richie said. "Steve's handling it."

"Fuckin' Texas. They don't forget nothin' down there," Hal said.

"Forget, or dig up?" I asked.

"What's that mean?" Richie asked me, his eyes narrowing.

"You know what I mean. Stuff you go looking for against people with the wrong color skin. Or the wrong accent. Your President's all about it," I said. I paused, surprising myself that I'd actually just said the words almost as an accusation against my best friends.

"*My* President? I don't know, Toby. Seems like you had a coupla dozen of us in your pickup headin' for that rally in Youngstown back in 2016. Yellin' our brains out. MAGA hats for souvenirs. Lotsa fist thumpin' and "Lock her up" and 'Build that wall!"

I was quiet for a moment. Remembering why I had voted for this guy who turned out to be such a dumbshit. But it wasn't like the other side gave us much of a choice, with all the free health care and bathroom rights for predators to hide in and regulations on small business. I had my construction company and was barely making it. Didn't need to be paying for free birth control for guys' wives and such.

"Maybe I did vote for him," I said slowly. "Doesn't mean I like everything he's always on about in that Twitter now. And how he talks about women, or other veterans like us."

"Yeah, the insults on McCain and the way the farmers are hurtin'—" Hal broke in.

"But sure as shit my vote wasn't about showin' up at the door of decent folk like Luis—"

"—and haulin' his ass away," Hal finished my sentence.

"Then what was it?" Richie asked us.

"You know—jobs. Decent wages. Factories reopening. Our towns how they used to be when we were growin' up. Cleaning up D.C. so they'd stop ignoring hardworking people."

"Yeah. All. Those. Illegals. Taking our jobs," said Brice, jabbing his finger in the air.

I glared at Brice, and he lowered his hand. "Except now I'm realizing they ain't takin' our jobs. Ain't no good jobs to take." I paused to eye my posse for a reaction. "Guys like Luis—and you know this—are cleaning motel rooms. Workin' in the car wash. Running a diner. Few of 'em are workin' construction, but they're the hardest goddamn workers I got on my payroll, so I got no beef."

"Yeah, but they bought The Coffee Spot! Someone coulda made a good livin' runnin' that place, right?" Brice said, looking around for guys to agree with him.

"Old Man Statler had The Spot up for sale for more'n a year," I reminded them. "No one wanted it. Not even so their teenage kids could wait tables, get some work experience. Not a bit of interest. Until Luis and Lupe came along and offered him cash." The guys grumbled, but they had to admit I was right.

"Damn. Never took Luis for one of *those* illegals," Brice said.

"Yeah. He spoke English real good," Richie said.

"I saw him and his family at church most Sundays," Hal said. "Helped me change a tire in a rainstorm last spring up on route 143."

"Marijuana, though. That's a crime," Brice said.

I was astonished when Richie weighed in. "Don't make me spit. I may be a cop, but you and I both know there's a half a dozen guys sittin' right here got a stash a weed from their kids in their back pocket to help with their back pain, and another half a dozen hangin' out at the VFW Hall been usin' it for their PTSD. Don't gimme this 'marijuana and crime' bullshit."

"Yeah, Luis is good people. He's not like those dangerous ones rapin' and killin' that you hear about. The ones we gotta stop at the border. The ones outta control with guns and gangs," Hal said.

I looked around at guys who *knew* Luis was one of the good ones. No different from us.

"What do we do now?" I finally asked.

I put the truck in gear and drove slowly along fields just beginning to bust out in green. I drove by the Field of Dreams here in our Croydon, Ohio. It's where we coached Little League together, me and Luis. My son Toby Jr.; his daughter Luisa. I know, a girl. But playing shortstop, at third base, nothing got by Luisa. I mean, fast on her feet, like a flash. And her arm? She fired that ball like a boss, burning up our first baseman's glove. Then she'd do that twirl—one brown arm pointing up at the sky, one leg bent up at the knee behind her. And when she came out of it, that pointing finger came straight at her father and me, and all three of us made the "yes!" fist pump together.

Luis had skin creased with sun and hard work, his eyes squinty, big hands knotted with calluses. Sturdy as a fire hydrant—never even put on a padded vest playing catcher if we were short a player; laughing at those times when a fastball struck him right in the heart.

"I'm fine, *amigo*," he'd tell me. "I've had worse pain listenin' to Lupe yell at me for bein' late for supper." He had that storytelling way, where you'd start laughing halfway through, just because – I don't know, his singsongy voice, how he made fun of himself, things he'd notice around town, like the town clock that had never worked, stuff that didn't make sense or had been around Croydon so long the rest of us never thought to question it.

As I drove I thought about Lupe too. How Marsha and Lupe ran the hot dog stand at the ballfield all season long. Lupe made a chili for the hot dogs that people lined up for twelve deep, even if it'd been years since they had kids playing ball. Just townsfolk standing around visiting with the neighbors, catching an inning or two, gossiping and goodwilling it up on those long summer evenings when the air was thick with mosquitoes and sweat. Marsha said it never felt like work with Lupe. Said Lupe told stories half in English, half Spanish, with sayings from her country back home. Like if snakes grew legs and could walk—that was Lupe's way of saying something impossible would never happen.

I walked inside the house to find Lupe and her three, plus Marsha and our three all eating pizza in the kitchen. I sat down too, and all of us were quiet, the three adults careful to chew and swallow and put on faces that hid the true concern behind our eyes. But I doubt the kiddos were fooled. The younger three went outside, and the three older ones went down the basement to play video games. Luisa, our star, stacked the dishes and rinsed the glasses before she joined my two boys downstairs. Slipping behind her mother's chair, she caught my eye, and I saw such a mix of emotions. Some I had seen before on the field, like grit and determination, and one I'd never seen: uncertainty. I pointed up and then right at her, like she always did, but I was the only one fist-bumping the sky.

At the town detention center a little after seven that night, I got what information I could from the official side.

"It's a shame, really," my buddy Steve said, gesturing for me to sit at his desk. "But we got the arrest order from El Paso and request for extradition. Don't matter that it's decades old. It's a warrant, and we had to move."

I stared at the name sign on his desk: 'Assistant Deputy Sheriff Steven Voltzthick.' For a minute, I wondered what country *his* family had come from originally.

"You tellin' me Luis was a drug dealer in another life?" I said. "Give me a fuckin' break."

Steve shrugged. "Arrested in a loading zone back in 1990 with his brother and a few others. Same last name. They had a few ounces a weed. Luis never showed up for his court date. He fled, left a bench warrant open all these years."

"But Luis don't even drink. We'll be havin' a few beers with the guys and Luis never even has a one. Like ever. Told me he didn't have the stomach or the wallet for drugs or alcohol. And that's been *years* since I've known him."

"What can I tell you? Look, I know he's your friend and gave a lot of effort to bein' a good citizen around town. But I don't choose who to lock up, you know?"

"I know." I kicked at the beat-up leg of Steve's desk. I wanted to do worse— to him, to the assholes in Texas who thought it was a good idea to go back decades in time and across a thousand miles to ruin the life of a good man. But I needed to keep my cool to help Luis. "Listen, let me pay his bail, get him home to his family. We'll help him get a lawyer. All the guys are down to be character witnesses. Write letters on his behalf."

But there was Steve fiddling with his pen, looking at me like I had two horns growing outta my head. "There's no bail. Aren't you listening? It was arrest *with extradition*. Luis'll be sent to El Paso in the morning to stand trial in immigration court, prolly get himself deported back to Mexico before the week is out."

"Jesus Christ. You kiddin' me?" I knew it wasn't Steve's fault, but I pounded on his desk with my fist. "He's got his family here, The Coffee Spot, his house. They can't just deport him. How does he come back?"

"He doesn't," Steve told me, stacking and re-stacking a pile a papers next to his phone. "It's the Zero Tolerance policy." He lowered his voice, glanced over his shoulder. Two other deputies sat across the room at another desk, drinking coffee out of paper cups, pointing at a computer screen, ignoring us. "Washington D.C. since the election ain't the same D.C. we been dealin' with over the years. They want what they call 'a more aggressive effort' to find illegals and deport them. Luis is gone as of tomorrow at 7:00 AM, and he ain't comin' back."

I wanted to vomit. A searing pain throbbed in my ears, reminding me of the inner pounding I woke up to every day that six months I spent in Kuwait during Desert Storm and for six months after I got back. Then as now, I felt it in my brain, my chest, my teeth too. Relentless, like a jackhammer. I'd been proud to serve in my country's military then, been proud ever since. But I wasn't proud of this. What would I say to Lupe and her kids?

"I need to see him," I was finally able to say, and Steve, unlocking the keys at his belt, led the way to the back of the building. Steve tapped on the small glass pane in the dented metal door before unlocking it. Luis, seated on an aluminum cot, his big hands clasped, looked up, his eyes two deep pools of sadness.

"You're not really allowed visitors, but Toby bein' an old friend to both of us, I figure you can talk for a few minutes back here where no one can see."

Luis stood up, and Steve handcuffed him, leading him outta the cell to a dim room with fluorescent lighting. It smelled like ammonia, piss, and mildew. Steve cuffed him to the table leg and helped him sit on a metal chair. "Ten minutes. I'll be back."

I had no words for my friend, and honest to God, I had to swallow numerous times to keep my own goddamned self from crying.

Luis spoke first. "Toby, you been such a good friend. I trust you. This is bad, no? Tell me what they told you."

"That you had drug charges from Texas, from 1990. That you didn't show up for court. They been waitin' to find you all these years."

"I thought all that was behind me," Luis said softly. He shifted in his chair.

"Drugs, man? What were you thinking?"

"I was fifteen. My cousins were delivery mules for some homies of theirs who had a pretty good marijuana business. They tried to recruit me. But I promised my mom I wouldn't get mixed up in drugs if she'd let me leave Sonora for *El Norte*. I saw real quick that if I stayed in El Paso, I'd get tagged, but I stayed long enough to catch a ride home one night, and that's when we got jacked up."

"Why'd you skip court?"

"A *compadre* told me since I was a minor, it was no big deal. That I'd just go to juvie for a couple weeks, no more, no record. But I was impatient, stupid, angry. I knew I hadn't done nothin' wrong, but I thought no one would believe me. So I ran. To Chicago first, and then down here, where I met Lupe." Luis looked confused, like he was waiting for the punchline of a joke he didn't understand. "Toby, I lived my whole life provin' I wasn't no scumbag drug dealer."

My chest ached, as if someone had shoved a combat boot into my rib cage. No breath, no mercy. In construction, things always go south. A framing beam collapses, a cement floor sags. And I'm always the guy with a plan. But here, looking at the face of my friend, I had nothing. And he could see it clear as I felt it.

"They're sendin' me back to Texas, right? And from there you think to Mexico?"

"Look, you gotta delay somehow. Tell 'em you got a business, a mortgage, kids born here. We'll get letters from everyone sayin' how you run the diner, coach teams, go to church. They'll see what a good man you are…" I couldn't help it. I choked up. Luis comforted me, can you believe it? Sonofabitch patted *me* on the back, as if in that moment forgiving me for not being able to help him.

When he spoke, it was almost a whisper. "It's better for Lupe to stay here with the kids, have a better life, even without me."

"She'll want to be with you."

"I know. But I gotta think about what's best for my kids. Mexico isn't safe. The life I made for them, it's here."

I could see the handcuffs were already creating red rings in his flesh, cutting into his wrists and bruising them, drawing blood. Jesus.

"What would you do?" Luis asked me. "The U.S. has so much more to offer. And my kids—they're born here, they're Americans."

What *would* I do? The truth was, I didn't have to choose: my kids or my happiness; their future, or mine. I could do both, have both. Raising them, coaching them, providing and taking pride. All of that was being taken away from Luis. I could only shake my head, look down at the floor, into a future that only reflected back the darkness. My loss. His kids' loss. Our town's loss.

"If they stay, you have my word that me and Marsha'll do everything we can to help. They'll be like family."

Luis gripped my shoulder with his big hand. "I know God has a plan. I just gotta stay faithful. He's blessed me like a hundred times. Look, he gave me you for a friend."

Steve came back just then to lock Luis up, but he had the decency to help him to his feet. I bit the inside of my cheek, hard. I blinked, and swallowed, and don't know how I actually made it outta that building.

When I got back in the truck, I rested my arms over the steering wheel and dropped my head, leaning in close to catch my breath. I stayed there the better part of an hour until I was composed enough to drive home.

At dawn the next day, I was up early and outta the house before Marsha and the kids were awake. Because of the early chill, I grabbed my vest and a cap from the back bench of the cab before I stood in the driveway leading from the jail to the highway. I didn't know if Luis would be able to see me as they drove him out of town, but I wanted to be a witness. I stood at attention for a good man.

I held my hand over my heart in a show of respect as a white van with tinted windows turned out of the parking lot and picked up speed on the highway. I had a thought—but I pushed it away. That our just wanting to be left alone to run our businesses, get back the factory jobs, no PC bullshit—just a return to all we once had—how had it all gone wrong? We were no better off. Lupe was right, and snakes could grow legs. This country was discarding a good man into the cold desert along our southern border.

I still wanted to Make America Great Again, like my ballcap said, but I also never meant for my friend to be 'the collateral damage,' as we used to say in Kuwait when civilians got killed by weapons that were never meant for them.

In mid-July as the season was ending, Marsha told me Lupe had her hands full because one of the boys was sick, and to give Luisa a ride home after the game. Luisa and I worked in silence. We picked up sno-cone wrappers, popcorn tubs, and the odd lost mitt. I'd been coaching Luisa the way me and her dad always did, challenging her to improve and allowing her to exercise her natural leadership over the other players.

We piled the bases on the wheelbarrow. At home plate, I looked up to find Luisa, her head tilted to the side, hands on her hips.

"Why do you still wear that cap?" she asked.

"What?"

"That ball cap you always wear. You don't even wear our team cap. You wear that stupid hat instead."

I reached up to take off the red hat. The brim was faded, the inside grimy from all the use. "It doesn't mean that much to me anymore."

"I don't think you even know how much it hurts me and my mom to see it."

"C'mon, Luisa. You and your mom are like family to me."

"You still don't get it, do you?" Luisa kicked the dirt with her cleats. "The government came to get my dad. But you voted for them to do it." She turned and started walking to the parking lot. Over her shoulder she said, "I'm just gonna call a friend to pick me up."

I jogged over to her. "Luisa. I'm sorry. You have no idea how sorry. I miss your dad too."

She gave me that look that no opponent at the plate could ever stare down. "Yeah. He was your friend. But He's. My. Dad. You got another friend? Probably. But I don't have another father."

Wink

MOHINI MALHOTRA

WE EYE THE METAL SHELVES—cans of green beans, yams, cranberry sauce, corn, black beans, garbanzo, pinto, baked beans, Progresso soups, boxes of pasta, bags of rice, dried beans…stacked and piled by type. Other volunteers are loading bags off trucks and out of car trunks in the parking lot, and another group is sorting through them and creating separate piles of clothing, housewares, and books. Families are filling shopping carts with goods, an elderly man is picking through coats and gloves, a woman is holding a baby, with a little girl in a too-large bright pink coat trailing her in the book section.

"Any guidelines? How much of each item per bag?" I ask the volunteer co-ordinator.

"Whatever you think makes a meal for four. Just pick and choose from the shelves. I always put in a dessert if there are any available." She leans in close to me and cups her mouth. "I tend towards generous."

We are making good on my New Year resolution—Sean, my teenage son, and I will volunteer more in 2020. And chalk up a few community service hours for Sean while we're at it.

We keep our jackets on, it is so bitterly cold, and start with the meal bags. I shake out paper bags from the bag bin and line them up neatly. "I'll count out the food and you bag it, works? Let's begin with pasta. Then we can add at least three cans of green beans to each one. Look how many there are."

"Do people buy them to donate to shelters? Why would they buy what they don't like to eat?" Sean queries.

Wow, he heard me, even through those earplugs which have become body appendages. "Who knows? Here's a can of corn, a can of black beans, a large can of soup, and a can of tomato sauce per bag."

"Mom, the lady said to add in a dessert. I see only four boxes of cake mix."

"Use them. We'll fill the rest with cranberry jelly, yams, apple sauce, lots left over from the holidays. *Note to self—next time you buy to donate, buy a lot of the same stuff—easier on the volunteers to make decisions. And…do not buy canned green beans.*

"Forget it, they expired…in 2015."

"Good you checked. Look at this artisanal pasta, I've seen it at Whole Foods for twelve bucks. Wow who would donate that? Oops, expired. Quinoa bags, expired. Barbeque sauces, expired. Here are rice noodles and plastic bags of flattened dried items, what are they? Great, only written in Chinese or Korean or whatever. Forget that! Here's a restaurant-sized jar of Spanish olives, several jars of marinated sundried tomatoes, grilled artichokes, Jamaican jerk-chicken spice rub…"

I look up and the little girl is twirling around in the middle of the room, her arms stretched out, her pink coat fanning out around her.

"Mom, when do we eat? I'm starving."

"It's only eleven. When we're done here. Want to go to our usual place in Bethesda?"

"I'm hungry now. I'm gonna eat this KIND bar. There's only one anyway." He's about to unwrap it, and I shout, "Put that down! That could be breakfast for a child. Hey, you can be hungry for an hour. Imagine how many kids go hungry for much longer."

Sean throws it back on the shelf, grabs two finished meal bags and marches them to the pickup counter. The little girl swallowed by the big pink coat has stopped twirling and is staring at us. Her two braids are flying out of her winter hat. Her wide dark eyes peek from under the faux fur lining. I slide the KIND bar into a meal bag, slowly lift up the only bag of chocolate chips and solo large plastic bottle of apple juice, lower them into the bag, and walk it to the counter. I point to it and wink at her. She hides a smile inside her jacket.

"Now on to toiletries," I say to Sean, observing the girl out of the corner of my eye. She's hopping and skipping towards the counter.

My son packs toiletries to a beat only he can hear. We put together over a hundred and twenty toiletry bags in an hour. I am finishing up my last one, rummaging in the shampoo bin, and I see a small bottle, *Oribe, Gold Lust Repair and Restore*. Can it be? My hairdresser was just talking about it when I went in for my color touch-up last week. I had googled it… $154 for a bottle. This is a two-oz. sample, the only one amidst many shampoos. Some poor woman or man wouldn't know its worth. And they are already getting such fancy products. I smell it—a bouquet of watermelon, lychee and flowers floats into the air. My hair gets so dry in the winter. That's why she recommended this. Besides, only one person would get it, and that just feels unfair. The volunteer coordinator has her back turned to me. My son has gone back to packing a few more meal bags—we've run out of Ziplocs.

I slide it into my coat pocket and glance around. There's that little girl in the pink jacket with the crazy braids flying out of her hat. She's clutching a meal bag in front of her with both hands and watching me. I look at her. She winks.

Proverbs for 2020

GREGORY LUCE

Objects in Mirror Are Closer Thank They Appear

They're behind you, yes, but
don't run, just walk briskly
and look ahead, they're
a shadow, it will always
be there but it's harmless
as long as you don't fall backward.

You Don't Need a Weatherman to Know Which Way the Wind Blows

It blows in your face
whichever way you turn
at first but don't worry,
trim your sails, tack
into the wind, you'll
soon have it pushing
you straight along.

The Life You Save May Be Your Own

You've heard it
a million times: put your
own mask on first. No one
else can do it for you,
at the very least you
have to want it.

Death Tie

DAVID LOTT

there's a death tie
in my closet
it's not meant to be a depressing thing
it's just that I'm really bad
at tying ties
so I leave one
already done up
dangling from the naked neck
of a wooden hanger

I never wear a tie to work
and rarely get invited to weddings anymore
so the tie tends to be for funerals
it's mostly for death

life
you could say
would mean its undoing

Seasonal Depression

STEVEN LEYVA

Give the termites your worry / about affording the rent. They too / are saying, *eat / the rich*. Two kids up / the block slash a neighbor's tires / while the elderly /couple are away at a wedding. Why / do I even bother to tell / anyone who's listening / that everyone involved was white / except me? Give the newborn / mosquitos their banquet of blood and your worry / about diabetes and rotted teeth. Who can say / what insectivore / is waiting / to eat the things that eat / your worry. Joy: the long tongued sloth / or joy: the pitcher / plant. Given the insistence on phoenix your tendons return to / given the moles that arrive / on your neck / year after / year from your grandmother / given the fact / that every elegy fails / to reach its true audience / why do I bother / to slash and slash and slash / white from this page?

Manassas Battlefield

JONATHAN LEWIS

Beyond the stretched shadows
of Henry House Hill,
beyond the cold cannons
in the golden fields,
two trees rise up
from crackling grass:
an old black cherry
outfitted in smooth bark,
forced against the fleecy trunk
of an eastern red cedar.
Their bodies now intertwined,
as saplings they must

have grown in parallel.
Then as juveniles, they jostled
over this tiny parcel of land
in a subterranean war
of roots, spilling forward
like infantry. Eventually
they reached a standstill,
two giants, now keeping
joint vigil over this quiet space
where so many fell to the earth.
Huddled as one, they share
a small breadth of peace.

The Hill

NATHAN LESLIE

"WHY DON'T YOU WORK that hill," Mrs. Whitten said. It wasn't a question.

She pointed up the slope past the woods towards the Miller's corn field hexagon. Her "estate," as she called it then, was just outside of town, but it felt like somewhere else.

I hurried to the barn and emerged with the trimmer, slipped my goggles over my glasses and started bushwhacking the hill. It was a sizable job. Mrs. Whitten said the kids liked it—"best sledding hill in town." She had a generous spirit, I could tell. I'm a decent read of people. She was kindly to her core, though she enjoyed the visceral feeling of being in control.

I had a half gallon of water in a milk carton sitting in the shade.

It was hot and humid, and the gnats peppered me from the woods. Dust and grass thwacked my face.

Every molecule in my body told me to get out of there. But I had to think big picture. I had few friends and no respect; my marriage was in ruins; and my daughter was about to turn four and she barely knew me, and the only way I could change that was to do whatever Mrs. Whitten needed me to do. Money. I felt on edge, and for some reason my hands shook. She was the key. And the key to the key for that moment was that hot, dusty hill gnarled with thistle and ragweed. My whole life was there.

I completed the job as the sun slanted down the horizon. Everything looked silhouetted and beautiful as I walked back to the manor. Mrs. Whitten was sitting on the porch drinking iced tea, cold crescents clinking in her glass.

"Did you finish up already?"

"I did at that," I said. "Yes, ma'am."

"Put everything back where you found it, and I'll see you tomorrow."

"Thank you," I said. I half bowed. I didn't want to say too much or ask too many stupid questions. She was already kind enough to bring me on board. I knew she didn't actually need me. I needed her far worse.

I put the goggles, gloves and trimmer back in the barn and stood there for a minute just feeling the heat radiate off me. I was dying for a drink of something cold and a bath. Both would have to wait.

Then I called Stevie, and he came and got me. We didn't talk much on the ride back. I was glad my efficiency had a window unit. Small blessings.

I had been in the pen for eighteen months. There were things I would talk about and things I wouldn't talk about. Most wouldn't even find out about the eighteen months, but if I knew you well enough, I might give it up.

Thing was I didn't *have* any real friends—nobody who mattered enough. The friends I *did* have didn't want to talk to me any longer. They blamed me. I was banned from homes—talk about a shitty feeling. My family was a help, but even they held me at arm's length.

I found out about Mrs. Whitten through the moving company I worked for prior—two months of sweeps across the county. Hard labor, boy. I was forty-seven years old, and I was having a hard time keeping up with the twenty-year-olds. My back barked at me. I felt *weary* around them, and then they found out—which made it harder. We mowed the yard of the Millers', and Mr. Miller asked Chuck, our crew chief, if anybody needed some odd jobs. Chuck looked right at me. I was grateful. I'd take all the odd jobs I could get. Work kept me out of the shadows.

At first it was just weekends—on top of the moving company—but then she hired me to do work around the house "pretty much full time," she said. Four times a week, minus Fridays when she had to be in the city. Handiwork, yard work, everything would be outside, she said. No men inside her house.

"I'm just not able to do everything," she said. She explained that her husband died two years ago, and she just didn't want to give everything up.

"I can do little jobs."

She knew nothing about me, as far as I knew.

The next day I was back on site at the normal time. I arrived a bit early, so I waited around until she came out onto the porch. That's the way she liked it.

"Can we take care of the windows today? Everything you need is out in the shed."

She called it the "shed." Perhaps this way she would make me feel less insufficient.

I found the ladder, Windex, rags and started in. It was a large undertaking, as the manor was an old Victorian with three stories, dormers and multiple windows. If I was smarter, I would've been scared, but I didn't even think about it.

Instead, I watched Mrs. Whitten when I could see her. I hadn't, at that point, been invited inside the house itself, so this was the closest I had come. I memorized the interiors—what I could see.

At one point, when I was cleaning the sitting room windows, Mrs. Whitten walked into the room and sat in a winged-back armchair. She was immersed in looking through a box of photographs, her eyes tight. When she looked up to catch my gaze, I glanced away.

I'm sure she had to wonder about me, even though she was a few decades older than I was. She reminded me of something, someone.

If she could've seen into my head, she would've known what I had been through. I learned things. I had the ability to take everything she had, like that. But I knew I had to restrain that impulse with every muscle I had.

My cousin Stevie understood me; he had gone through something similar a few years back. We weren't close, but I viewed him as a kind of model. His life was scoured clean, and he patched it back together from the basement up. At that time he had a decent job at a hardware store, where he had worked for several years.

There was a day I showed up fifteen minutes late. Mrs. Whitten was on the porch waiting for me, running her palm along the painted white rail. She must've been beautiful in her own day; I could see that. She kept her hair done up in a bun, and I was thinking it would look better down on her shoulders, flowing.

"Good morning, Ray," she said. I nodded.

"Are you planning on arriving late frequently? If so, I won't be needing your services, to be perfectly frank."

I explained what happened, or tried to, but she just raised her palm up, as if to say, "I don't need to hear any more." So I stopped mid-sentence.

"I truly apologize," I said. "It won't happen again."

Mrs. Whitten squirreled up her right eye and swallowed. She told me I needed to help her repaint the shed. This was good news because if I was smart, I could work in the shade for most of the time, I realized. My skin felt leathery and baked-in already.

I could smell the lilacs around Mrs. Whitten's porch. For a moment I almost felt dizzy from the aroma.

It took me five days to prime and then fully repaint the barn. I wasn't in a hurry and, in fact, I took my time—dragging out the process and taking long breaks.

I happened to finish on a Friday, which was the day when she was supposed to pay me for my week's work. She had paid the two previous weeks in cash. She did the same that day. Stevie was waiting for me. He didn't know.

I was standing on the porch steps watching her glass of white wine bead up and sweat. I watched the condensation drip onto the table, though the stem stayed dry. Something collapsed inside of me.

I walked up the stairs and the porch itself—it felt like forbidden territory. A knot in my gut. White paint and sunshine, standing on the manor house proper. I didn't think; I just walked straight into the house. I was sunbaked and needed a cool dark place.

I was inside the foyer—rugs and little statues and paintings on the walls. I just stood there, leaning slightly against the wall.

When Mrs. Whitten turned the corner, cash in hand, she started. I watched her swallow.

"Now what are you doing?"

"I'm hot," I said. "Do you have something cold I could drink?"

But when she reached out to hand me the money, I clutched her wrist instead. I don't know why I did it. Something about her earring sway. Something about a tickle in the back of my throat.

It *felt* like an accident, though it wasn't. I knew that.

I knew, of course, the mistake I was making. Unredeemable. But I was not myself. The sun had fried my good thinking. I was outside of myself—someone else was operating my body.

"And where is the rest of it now?" I yelled. My other hand rose upward. I could see the shadow of it before I let it fly. There was a moment when I knew I had to stop, that I could still keep this from being the worst thing, but I couldn't. My hand fell, and again.

She had barely anything, which made it even worse. And I knew I had to leave right away. I didn't tell Stevie about my misstep. Instead I asked to hear some blues on the radio. Something to calm my nerves. But he couldn't find any. The closest was some old Lynyrd Skynyrd on a station with lots of ads about jewelry and expensive resorts. I had him drop me off at the bus station.

"I have to meet someone," I explained.

"You want me to wait? I can wait."

"No, go on. I'll get a lift."

I had enough for a ticket to the middle of the country. I had done plenty wrong in my life, and it was time to pay. I bought a hamburger at the fast food stand inside the station and boarded the bus.

"No bags?" I shook my head.

Only invisible ones, I thought.

But two weeks later, I was under wraps all over again. I laid low, grew a beard, slept out under the stars, in the woods, in caves. I bought some cheap sunglasses and avoided public places. I snuck into town to buy food at the little grubby market. It was no way to live.

I still don't know how they found me. Might've been my phone. I should've tossed that thing in the station garbage can when I had the chance. Just that thin little filament is all they needed, I guess.

Too bad.

Part of me was almost thankful though. I was down to my last couple of dollars and was getting the runs bad, drinking from the creek out back when I became desperate. Even though I knew where I was headed, I also knew they had to feed me and there was a sink. I could drink as much water as I liked, which is all I wanted.

Someday I'd count my blessings and be a good man, I thought. I was in the car and the blue lights were whirling. I don't know why—they already had me. It wasn't an emergency. I felt the cool air conditioning against my cheek, and I had a pebble in my mouth to keep my saliva going until I could drink something again. They didn't take that from me, oddly.

I said nothing, turning my tongue over the stone over and over.

Last Epistle

KATEEMA LEE

If I die suspiciously, please know
I didn't kill myself. If you read
my statuses, emails and tweets,
testimonies to tiresome days and anti-
climactic nights, know I knew life
was more tepid creek than volcano.
I wouldn't jog my daily route then dive
into dark water, and if by chance I fell in,
I would grow gills. I wouldn't shape
ropes out of bags or dare any savior
to take my life.
                       Melancholy
is not preface to death. Black or brown
is not prologue to demise. My birth
is not precursor to my passing
too soon. If I disappear,
look for me.

Sincerely,
[Unnamed]

Invisible Woman

MARY ANN LARKIN

I am vanishing
from men's dreams,
from their poems.
I no longer lie in
"the sheltered bed
near the cypress-trees,"
my hair golden, my eyes
voluptuous, dark love-bites
on my neck. Men see no
"wild doves fluttering
in my soothing breasts."

It was comfortable there
under the cypress.
I knew what to wear. The word
diaphanous comes to mind.
I did not need to speak.
I thought I'd die riding
that long slow wave,
easing their desperation.

It took a while to notice
I was gone. I still don't know
where I went. Invisible women
may not need a place. Perhaps
this is freedom. I was always
curious. It is lighter. I'm like air.
Love looks now like a long path.
Grass grows in the middle,
winds away in a sweet curve.
No one's hot breath whispers: Wait.

I'm Not Sorry, America

LEN KRUGER

THE SHOW IS CALLED: I Hate Myself: America's Most Self-Loathing. Contestants stand in front of a studio audience and spend 60 seconds recounting a shameful episode from their past, a persuasive piece of evidence that supports their uncompromising self-hatred.

The ratings are huge. I am a contestant. Opening rounds. Much fluff eliminated: a story about forgetting someone's birthday, about standing up a first date, about hitting a parked car and not leaving a note. Please. I go with how I betrayed a lifelong friend three separate times—as a child, a teen, and an adult. Forsake, rinse, repeat! I say, sticking the finish. I make the semifinals. My philanthropic embezzlement story does the trick. No regrets, no apologies. America eats it up.

I advance to the finals. My opponent goes first, his mouth in a continuous smirk, fear simmering in his eyes. He goes old school, bragging how he broke all Ten Commandments in no particular order.

I can beat that. I spend all 60 seconds silent, staring at the studio audience, scanning their upturned faces, lips licked in anticipation of my spectacular perfidy. Behind me on stage, the bright neon sign flashes the franchise slogan: No Heroes, Only Villains. I leer at the blinking red light of the camera, I burrow into the hearts and minds of millions watching nationwide, I etch America's souls with their self-manufactured shame.

The votes are tallied. I win. All hail the bastard king. My reign will be long and full of sorrow.

On Common Ground in Westminster, MD

DANUTA E. KOSK-KOSICKA

The first hour is green grass and red
brick buildings. The shade evaporates.
Then the bagpipe and Indian
flute pull apart the sticky air

and burst in the 4th of July fireworks.
On the second day we begin to carve.
The gouge uncovers softness
in linoleum blocks. Like plowing a furrow

in the ground wherein seeds are sown.
The harvested grain turns into oblong
loaves rising under linen cloth. Whiffs
of fresh-baked bread, a genie

released from the bottle of time,
take us to other continents.
For five days we weave the words,
tie and untie roots, streams, rocks,

the Feathered Serpent and Celtic
knots. When the last evening arrives
on the stage we sing
our multivoiced poem.

The Invisible Walls

CHRISTOPHER KONDRICH

They built the invisible walls in front of walls we could see.
They built them along the roads and paths,
on either side of every river.
They made these new walls so we couldn't reach the old walls anymore.
They called the walls protection, but didn't say from what.
So we woke at night sweating
or we woke at night needing to sweat.
Our bodies dry and throbbing.
There were days when we spoke of the invisible walls
and days when we spoke of nothing else.
How they couldn't be chiseled into or chipped away at
or spray-painted on or scaled.
Our shoes wouldn't catch on anything
for us to lift ourselves up.
We were either walled off individually or together,
depending on who was asked
or what was considered to be bodily harm.
They built the invisible walls over time
so that we wouldn't know whether
there were once fewer walls
or whether they were there all along,
casting the old, visible walls like shadows.
We tried anticipating where the next walls would be
but they were always erected on the previous day.
And the day before that there were walls we wouldn't remember
seeing inside our homes, our bedrooms.
In front of our closet doors.
So we always have to wear the same clothes.

The New Normal

ELIZABETH KNAPP

Can someone please define "new normal?"
How does one even describe the new normal?

I admit I'm not quite ready for this, never
having adjusted to the old new normal

that descended after the first plane hit.
At that moment emerged a darker new normal

like something out of a horror flick. Drones
circled, invisible vultures, in the new-normal

skies, bomb-dropping ghosts, imaginary scores
of dead in their unmarked graves the new normal.

Now collectively, the world holds its breath.
One global exhale the death of new normal.

From across the street, my neighbor waves,
our social distance the law of new normal.

Hard to say which will kill us first—virus
or ignorance—civil war our new normal.

Binge-watching death tolls while baking bread—
new quarantine skills on display the new normal.

If this is the end, at least I can say I napped
& sang my way through the new normal.

Dear White Girl

HOLLY KARAPETKOVA

Dear errata. Dear apology. Dear sugar and spice, cherry and cherry pop. Dear pillar of salt, pillar of the plantation, love and charity to all. Dear Barbie doll in a permanent ball gown, Barbie Dream House and who'd she have to marry to end up there. Dear laurel tree and hollow reeds. Dear sorrow-become-stone, caged-in-the-forest, turned-into-a-bird. Dear picked flowers, wild and domesticated. Dear Wyoming and Louisiana and 81 cents to the dollar. Dear Scylla and Charybdis, Good Witches of the North and South, Governor's wife, Overseer's wife, CEO's wife, slumlord's wife. I didn't mean what I said. Please don't let me end up with that old maid card in my hand.

Southern Living

HOLLY KARAPETKOVA

Without Sanctuary: Photographs and Postcards of Lynching in America

I turn to leave
but it is always sunset.

The shadows stretch,
each knuckle a knot,

each tree a body
shifting in the wind.

In the postcard photograph
white faces crowd in to watch;

I cannot see their features
clearly enough to know

I am not among them.
On the back a photo credit,

a county and state, proof
of witness.

Sometimes a note.
Coon cooking.

All OK and would like
to get a post from you.

Then a scrawled signature,
a name and address:

Strike a match
and we all go up in smoke.

Sea Change

BETH KANTER

"WHAT IF THE JOURNEY kills us?" she asks him night after night. "If we stay, surely they will put us in the ground" is how he answers her each and every time.

So they leave, two more huddled masses sailing from old world to new. The newlyweds carry their tightly bundled life on board: candlesticks, prayer shawl, brown-crusted bread, hand-stitched lace, a family ring tightly sewn into the band of her thick wool skirt.

On day three, as she begins to form pickle green and sky blue dreams of home, she is yanked awake by the sound of her name. "Anna," her young husband whispers before clutching his chest. In that moment she knows that pleasantly shaded dreams will never find her or her sleep again.

Up on deck, clean air brushes against her face for the first time since setting sail. The salty spray stings her cheeks and turns the tip of her nose a raw, fiery red. She watches as four queasy strangers hurl her husband into the deepest of graves. His eyes wide open. Shoes still on his feet.

The ocean's rage dampens the sound his clothed body makes when it smacks the sea. Jagged waves use him for a watery game of catch.

"See," she wants to tell the man she'll never get to know. "They didn't put you in the ground."

Man overboard. Woman journeying on.

A/72/ L.2 Resolution

NUBIA KAI

> Necessity of ending the economic, commercial
> and financial embargo imposed by the
> United States of America against Cuba.

The Debate

The arms of the octopus are angry,
green with envy and hate
that its colored baby doll
ran away from home
and built a house of her own
on the Bimini streams of the Caribbean
of gold rock and pearls winding
a footpath to a temple of tenacity,
the one we found at the doorsteps
of this concretized dream.

It was right under our eyelids.
It was right under our shoeless, calloused feet
feeling the riches of the earth.
It was right under our nose
smelling the mariposa and hibiscus.
We reached out our hands
took the scent and soil and vision,
fashioned it the way God fashioned Adam
into the women and men
we wanted to be.

We did this
as the world watched entranced
at the unfolding miracle
of orchids replenishing the mangrove swamps
breaking the hurricane's back
with the sickle and hoe singing in unison

implanting fruits so sweet
we share with the toilers with joy.

See the butterfly jasmines they toss
on our shores in gratitude
like petals adorning the nuptial bed of nations.
See the bee hummingbird,
the smallest bird,
the smallest frog,
the smallest moth be giants today
in word and deed
hurling the hurricane arms of the octopus
around its mendacious throat.
Cuba si, bloqueo no.
It has already happened.

East Barre

REUBEN JACKSON

The salesclerk claimed
that the snowfall spoke
with a Vermont accent.
I only knew
that the cords I bought
from LL Bean
had not been purchased in vain-
And that here, no one fought
for the last roll of toilet paper
On an otherwise empty shelf.
The latter was reason enough
to call my Southern kin-
Whose minds were likewise filled
With Central Casting notions
of the world above Boston.
But the weather owned my eyes
Like the gazebo at the foot of Main Street,
where I wept, waiting for Jimmy Stewart's ghost.

In Lieu of Graduation, May 2020

GARINÈ ISASSI

"FIRST YOU NAME ME 'Hripsime' and now this!"

"'Hripsime' was a saint and a martyr. Get your feet off the dashboard." Her mom swatted at Ripsy's shins with her non-driving hand where her legs bridged between the passenger seat and the glove compartment.

"She was a victim of sexual harassment and murder."

"Well, Ripsy, they didn't call it that in ancient Armenia."

Ripsy pulled her feet down. She twirled the graduation mortarboard hat between her index fingers. The tassel caught in the elastic of the facemask that dangled from her wrist like a courtier's handkerchief.

Since all high school graduation ceremonies were cancelled, Ripsy's mother, Sophie, had a grand idea to dress Ripsy up and parade her under the famous street sign, named after great-grandfather Levon of Simonian family lore, at the crossroad of Simonian Lane and Love Street. Mom would subsequently mortify her by posting it publicly on social media with a variety of hashtags. Mom, like all moms, didn't seem to understand that when she tagged Ripsy's Twitter name, @PippyRips, her schoolmates also saw it—some of whom followed Twitter accounts specifically for ammunition to cause social demotion at Quince Orchard High School.

Besides, Ripsy didn't feel like celebrating. The COVID-19 lockdown voided all the fun stuff too—no prom, no spring track team, no banquets—and left her with nothing but a ten-week stream of homework to finish out her high school years.

They turned off Route 15, onto Sabillasville Road, also known to Ripsy and her brothers as "Nowhereville Road." It snaked through Catoctin Mountain

Park, location of the famed Presidential Retreat, deliberately hidden in this po-dunk patch of Maryland so as not to be easily found. You couldn't even get cell phone reception here.

"So, do you think Camp David is that way?" Ripsy waved her hand across her mother's field of vision, with her middle finger shooting the bird.

"Stop!" Sophie cried, swatting again. "There's probably spy gear along here."

"Nowhereville Road" took them to open farmland on the other side of the park, almost to Pennsylvania, but not quite.

It had been over two years since they had come out here. Ripsy knew that when her mom was a kid, the family took a yearly photo under the signs. Once Ripsy and her brothers were born, they were dragged out here periodically for additional cheesy family endeavors. The only other time there was a solo photo of Ripsy in this backwater town was from her kindergarten graduation. Ob-viously, her mom would juxtapose the two graduation photo shoots against each other on social media, for heightened cuteness factor of the little girl and the big girl—#AllGrownUp!

"C'mon," Sophie cajoled, rolling down the window to let in the warm air. "It's fun. God knows we need something fun right now. "

Ripsy rolled her eyes, which sent her mother into lecture mode.

"My grandfather escaped a Stalinist work camp as a teenager—your age! Immigrated to the U.S. and built his farm up here with his own hands. He and my father worked hard to build the grocery store chain from nothing! He was so honored when they renamed the street after him."

Ripsy joined into her homily, so in unison, they said, "It was the first time Pop ever saw his father cry." Ripsy pulled the top part of her graduation robe away from the back of her neck. "Geez, this robe is itchy."

Her great-grandfather Levon began Smart Fruit Grocery as a stand next to his small farm. He priced on a sliding scale for local sharecroppers, wealthy trav-elers and the poorest vagabonds. Nobody mentioned that the only reason his produce ended up labeled "organic" was because he was, at first, too poor and then too cheap to invest in pesticides and farming chemicals. Ironically, now, Smart Fruit catered to the most affluent customers in the trendiest neighbor-hoods. Each store pretended old-world charm with market-researched, homey interiors and Depression-era photos of Levon at his fruit stand everywhere.

The tiny country crossroad was not only the site of the first Smart Fruit Stand, but also the first meeting of Pop and Nana, Sophie's parents. Nana and her family stopped to buy cantaloupe on their way to Harrisburg, immediately discovered that the Simonians were Armenian too, and the rest is history. They've been together for seventy-three years and even now held hands like they were still twelve years old on the fateful day they met.

As they turned on to Simonian Road, Sophie gasped and slowed the car. The vines and scrubby shrubs along one side of the road had been cleared. Orange cones and an electrical line took the place of the disappeared greenery.

"Mom? What the hell?"

"Sweetie, please don't curse," her mother distractedly advised.

Within fifteen feet of the intersection to Love Street, a parade-style barricade blocked Simonian Lane. Beyond it, the tree line along the right side turned into a chain-link fence. Both Sophie and Ripsy leaned forward in their seats as the car rolled to a halt.

"What the hell?" Sophie said. She grabbed her iPhone from the drink cup holder and checked for cell service, which she found.

In mirrored synchronization, they exited the car and walked to the barricade. Ripsy still had the mortarboard in her hand. The unzipped graduation gown billowed out behind her in a light breeze.

Where there used to be land behind a gentle line of trees, there was now an active farm behind a metal fence, topped with barbed wire. Ripsy followed her mom around the barricade as if in a trance. At least twenty people dotted the field, bent over spring-high corn stalks, apparently weeding the rows, their dark heads bobbing as they pulled unwanted seedlings of clover or dandelion.

"This isn't right," Sophie said. "Why wouldn't they use a tractor and soil cultivator?"

As they walked to the crossroad, watching the field, Ripsy realized that these workers were not normal farmhands. Many of them had long hair. They were silent, small and narrow shouldered. They were children.

Sophie ordered Ripsy to stand under the sign as she fiddled with her phone.

"Are you kidding? Isn't this beyond weird? Mom?"

"Don't you see the truck?" Her mother cast her eyes up Love Street, stepped back and ordered, "Smile!"

Ripsy turned to see a white Jeep Wrangler with a wide green stripe along the side coming toward them. Then she was distracted by one of the kids in the field standing up to full height. Then all of them were curiously looking toward Ripsy and Sophie.

Ripsy heard the click of her mother taking a photo or a video, then another and another. Ripsy turned and put on her graduation cap, doing dramatic fashion poses, even though she knew her mother was not focusing the lens on her. After each shot, Sophie fiddled with the touch screen.

"Mom," Ripsy's voice cracked a little through the fake smile she held on her face. "What should we do when they get here?"

Sophie stepped up close to her, taking her hand. Her mom was shaking slightly, even in the springtime sun.

"Follow my lead," Sophie pleaded, staring straight into Ripsy. "Like when we haggle with that farmer's market woman."

Ripsy nodded. Then Sophie began taking more photos, this time focusing on Ripsy with the phone, clicking away as Ripsy continued to smile and turn her head this way and that.

The jeep rumbled up and two uniformed ICE agents got out. Both wore facemasks.

"Excuse me, Ma'am," the taller one addressed Sophie, standing stiffly. "You are not supposed to be here." The shorter agent had freckles around his eyes, and he watched Ripsy as she covered her fake smile with the facemask that had been on her wrist this whole time.

"Oh!" Her mom put on her ditsy voice. "We're just taking some photos," She swept her arm toward Ripsy. "We love that this is called 'Love Street.'" She smiled at the man. Ripsy noted how her mom was the only one bare-faced of the four of them standing there.

"Yes, Ma'am." He relaxed slightly and said jovially, "My mom took a lot of photos when I graduated. May I see?"

He politely opened his palm toward Sophie, who stared at it a moment. Ripsy's heart raced. Sophie slowly handed over the phone, glancing back at Ripsy. The second agent stepped closer to look. Sophie leaned in too.

Ripsy took the chance to turn her back on them, keeping her head up, looking over the field, while reaching one hand through the black folds of her graduation gown to her own phone in her pants pocket.

After a moment, she heard Sophie say, "This one's cute, isn't it?"

The taller agent seemed startled and quickly said, "Ma'am, this is a restricted area, and we have to ask you to delete some of these photos."

"Oh no! I hope not this one?"

"These that show our facility in the background. I'm going to delete them." Which he immediately began to do, even clearing the backup folders in the phone's memory.

"But then we won't have any full shots with the signs!" She feigned a whiny demeanor.

"Mom," Ripsy echoed the same whine for full effect. "Did we come all the way out here for nothing?"

The men looked at each other with smirks in their eyes.

The agent holding her phone made an offer. "I'll take some of you together!"

Sophie clapped her hands, "OK!" she exclaimed. "Sweetie, come stand over here."

Ripsy came. They stood under the sign as the young officer turned his back to the field. The weeding activity resumed in the cornfield, but Ripsy saw the furtive glances in their direction. He took photos with the opposite side of the street in the background—green trees, even some wildflowers—and the street signs.

He then walked away from them, toward their car, which appeared abandoned on the other side of the barricade. It seemed to be their cue to follow. He appeared to be flipping through the images as he walked. Suddenly he stopped and stared at the phone. Ripsy's stomach knotted. She and her mom halted beside him.

"Here! You both look beautiful in this one!" He held the screen toward the mother and daughter, seemingly very proud of himself.

"Wow," Ripsy's clenched stomach turned to slight nausea, but she was genuinely surprised, peering into the phone. "That *is* a great picture! Weird. . ." she trailed off.

"Well, thank you so much!" Sophie swiftly took the phone back. "I guess we'll just head out now." Ripsy grabbed her mom's free hand and they speedwalked together around the barricade, only parting to dash into the front seats on either side of the car. As her mom turned the engine, she waved at the two men, who continued to observe them. She did a slow three-point turn and cautiously drove away.

Ripsy and her mom both sat stick straight in their seats, alternately breathing hard or not at all, and saying nothing. As Sophie turned back on to Sabillasville Road, she drove exactly the speed limit while Ripsy vigilantly watched the side of her mother's face.

As they left the no-cell-service zone of the park, Ripsy's pulled her phone out of her pocket, ready to show her mom the photos she secretly took of the kids in the field and even some of the agents during the two minutes they were occupied with deleting everything on Sophie's phone. Instead, it began to ping repeatedly. A flurry of twitter and instagram messages tagged with @PippyRips popped up, along with the hashtags #migrantchildrenarechildren, #whereare the-children and #familiesbelongtogether.

"Holy shit, Mom! What did you do?"

Sophie pulled into the Sheetz gas station, lurching to park at the far side of the lot.

She turned to Ripsy, her lower lip trembling, and said, "Sweetie, please don't curse."

Then Ripsy watched in stunned silence as her mom stumbled out of the car to the grassy area beyond the curb and threw up.

DISCOVERY PRIZE

Bull Sharks of Long Island Sound

NATALIE E. ILLUM

POETRY

My mother's green dress is a wound on our front lawn.
An ineffective fertilizer. *No one leaves home unless*
home is the mouth of a shark. Bite marks frame
our windows. The neighbors never lose their teeth.

No one leaves home unless
the next zip code over is full of chemicals.
Blood pools in the soil of their backyards.
Cancer attacks even the most effective fertilizer.

The rich don't know they're ingesting poison.
My father's elixir is Budweiser and Tequila.
Addiction is the most effective fertilizer
to drown a middle-class garden.

My parents turned our house into a riptide.
Her skirt is a pool of chum in the backyard
to kill any lingering flowers. *No one leaves home*
unless you find a lifeguard.

This town circles around its neighbors.
Our lawns bloom with fresh tumors.
I hinge on the sharp jaw of our secrets.
My home is the mouth of a shark.

*the italicized line in the first stanza is from the poem "Home" by Warsan
Shire

D.C.

DONALD ILLICH

I'd never seen rats
crawl down city streets
until I came here,
where presidents lied,

and people knew
how to take the fifth.
Now I fib with the best
of them, to my partner,

about where I was
and who I was with,
to my boss, who thought
I was sick for a week,

to the sky and ground,
which believed one day
my promise to end in them.
The rats understood.

They twitched the truth,
hid their falsehoods.
Just before they ran
across my booted feet,

they squeaked blood
inside their fat bodies,
left their feces
outside my door.

North South East West

EMILY HOLLAND

North

> Chocolate with the sweet cherry dip. Berry swirl coated in melted peanut butter. We can't eat our soft serve fast enough in the heat. It's the last good night of summer. Closing time for Humdinger's short north season. Blueberries and raspberries are ripe for picking now. In a field somewhere, birds are drunk on fermented juices. Their alcoholic laughter echoes in the fading twilight hour, our faces all messy with sugary drippings. Moths metronome against the fluorescent lights. Count us into a new season.

South

> In a small town somewhere south, adults park outside the Dollar General, count their cash before going in, know how many items each kid can walk out with. We took our allowance when it was given: rarely. Country roads like this leave few options for spending. A coloring book. Plastic yo-yo. Sometimes a pack of SnoBalls to stave off hunger on the drive back across town. The trips were always long. Early morning or dusk could look the same in the right light.

East

Early morning low tide. The fishermen with their poles and coolers out already, walking far into the shallow water. Drowsy waves barely break. Going east, it's easy to catch the light. Comes up there. We all know this. I dig with my toes for sleeping sand dollars. Before bleaching, they're dirty and alive. I want to know they're still down there somewhere. At the house where I should still be asleep, mom opens the bedroom door just a crack to see if I'm gone. Maybe it's the same thing.

West

The sun sets on the west, always the same thing. Desert knows no bedtime. Animals and birds poke out of their caves as the light fades cotton candy. Do they know the taste? The sweetness of it? How sugar sticks in the corners of my lips as I stare, open mouthed, at the sky. Somewhere a Ferris wheel goes round and round. Animals and birds poke out of their caves. Somewhere there's a girl whose skin bursts with honey when sunset sets in. She tastes as sweet as I remember.

Vacancy Inspection, Green Valley Road, Keymar, Maryland

MATT HOHNER

A small American flag stuck in a fencepost by the road hangs in tatters, disintegrated white stripes & stars rotted out from a blue field now the color of nightfall; the few red stripes left, once the color of blood, droop, aged & faded to pewter & tin. Delicate Queen Anne's lace, milkweed & chicory, lambsquarter & horseweed, dark pokeweed berries & crimson spears of curly dock all riot unchecked in the wrecked tangle of horse pasture out back by the barn. The insurgent wild claims its caliphate amidst the neighbors' manicured fields. Ashen, warped fence boards crack in the sun; weeds spill through the fence where the plywood shed leans at angles toward the ground.

There is no hay in the barn save for straw strewn about; horseshit's left in a few piles in corners—a parting gift to the creditors. The door swings wide to the air & wind, nothing left alive inside to shelter from weather or predators. Rabbit hutches bent & empty, stalls' floors swept & dry. A fishing net resting on a line of nails on the wall; BB gun collecting dust on a work bench. A red Radio Flyer wagon still as a corpse sits where it was last towed, the child's laughter long since disembarked. Cowboy boots worked sweat-soft & dingy slouch on a shelf next to a baling hook. An old liquid fire extinguisher tank rusts in a corner. Up in the hayloft, a tire swing sways gently like a pendulum in the warm breeze through gaps in the slat walls & warped tin roof, measuring the slow tic of abandonment, the half-life of memory.

Pushing past the broken patio door: piles of clothing & toys & countertop appliances in the basement, dumped there for the last haul in their flight away from the disaster. Bare rooms upstairs, the calendar on the kitchen wall last turned to a new month five years ago, dates circled, times, places, & peoples' names scribbled in squares they never got to cross off. Unfinished kitchen remodel, leather bomber coat slumped on a chair, boots & shoes on the floor of the closet by the front door. The earth twirled & traveled through space & the money dried up. The house became the bank's & the animals & humans all had to go. What remains: a thudding hush, cobwebs across the basement stairwell, the smell of stillness. A flag on a fencepost the color of bruises, the color of shrapnel.

Girl Suit

AMANDA HODES
—after Kristín Ómarsdóttir

They gather at the shopping mall to see her.
Wrapped around the set, kids hook candy canes
from their bottom lips like fish.

Beady eyed with Christmas lists stapled
to their foreheads, they came here for a prophet.
She aims to deliver,

sweats beneath the suit like a second skin.
The girls are rehearsed
and land on her lap like stones.

What do you want this year?
Hot breath on her face.

They want her thin arms, lashes,
her freckled nose, the way it turns up
just 40 degrees at the end.

Ballet flats stitched at the bottom
so they'll never tie shoes again.

She sighs and takes notes on the tops of their heads,
traces the seam where the zipper will be—
zig-zag part of a young girl's hair.

Emergency Vehicles Coming Through

ROBERT HERSCHBACH

Our roads are sized for catastrophe,
the cul-de-sacs like asphalt skating rinks,
built for fire trucks to turn in,
the layout in general a banner campaign
with a message for us all: *look, look,*
someday you too. I remember how a softball
slipped into a curbside drain when my son
was three: he hit it into the street
with his toy bat, and the slope was such
that it rolled automatically into that dark slot.
He couldn't believe it was irretrievable,
that there wasn't some way
to track a ball to the Chesapeake,
have it fished out, that it wouldn't
come bouncing up from somewhere
on our next trip to the beach. I couldn't explain
why Lost becomes part of the name
we have for some things,
and why the county wouldn't send a crew
to dig up the street for an $8.99 ball,
special as it was with its fuzz
and cheery orange color. How this
was just the beginning: some kinds of trouble
can't be fixed, not even by superheroes
flying to the scene on gleaming red trucks, and in time
we're all on close terms with such trouble.

Never Mind the Avalanche

KATHLEEN HELLEN

god says to hell with it
tepid winters worsting, spring's titanic
oceans, and everywhere the mischief
of the god of falling water

… and everywhere two streams
from the beginning

one supplies the master's joy of fish, the lights
across the street
giving rights to fetch the drink, rights
to clean, fresh quench

the other dammed or drowning, leaking
twinkle, makes you think
lead
protects lead

from snow melt and road salt
from run-off and flush
from chloride that rusts
the pre-frontals
lead

can trick you
the good hair in bagfuls
flushed

Angel in Pink

MELANIE S. HATTER

MAGGIE REACHED FOR ANOTHER Oreo and leaned back into the couch, dunking the cookie in her milk. She sucked on it before smooshing the sweet goodness into paste in her mouth. Next to her, Poppy lay sprawled, crushing Maggie's thigh. Her favorite actor was kicking in a door, gun drawn, in an old episode of *Criminal Minds*. She'd seen this one before but was just as eager to watch the story play out, see the good guys take down another perverted *unsub*.

A knock roused Poppy off the couch and she ran barking to the door, ears flopping madly. Maggie took a second before setting her glass on the table and moving slowly toward the door. She rarely received visitors, and when she did, they were well planned in advance. Peeking through the peep-hole, she saw a young girl dressed in pink. Maggie lifted Poppy into her arms, which always silenced the cocker spaniel, and opened the door.

"Please help." The girl's panic came through in a whisper. "My dad is hurting my mom. I need to call the police."

The words came in a flood, and for a second Maggie couldn't move. Her heart and breath stopped as the girl's crumpled face engulfed her own body. She dumped Poppy on the hardwood floor, and the dog ran in circles, letting out a few short barks as Maggie rushed to get the phone on the side table by the couch. The girl stayed at the door until Maggie beckoned her inside. "Just ignore the dog. She won't hurt you."

Without thinking, Maggie handed the phone to the girl, who appeared unsure of what to do with this bulky house phone that few people had in their homes anymore. Maggie took it back but hesitated before dialing 9-1-1. She'd never called the police before. Never had to. The last forty years had been blessedly benign. After high school, she'd studied business management at Bowie

State—had wanted to attend Texas Southern but couldn't afford the out-of-state fees. Had gotten a job at a marketing firm and had made a decent, though un-remarkable, career in that field. Never married—though if Warren had asked her, she would have said yes. But he hadn't. He'd dumped her after three years and married someone else the following year. Perhaps as a distraction or a salve, Maggie had raided her savings account, put a down payment on her townhouse, adopted a dog, and chose a life in which she never had to call the police.

She pressed the speaker button and let the girl explain the situation to the dispatcher. It was 8:52 p.m.

The front door was still open, though the screen door had closed. The girl paced back and forth by the coffee table as she spoke to the dispatcher, explaining where she lived and that her father was hitting her mom, that she had escaped the apartment and run. The girl wore no shoes, just fluffy pink socks. She was all chubby cuteness that belied the words coming from her mouth.

Before high school, Maggie's life had been less benign. Memories from that period had been buried so far down that what surfaced now felt like images from a television show. Her mother. Her father. She didn't want to remember.

Maggie's house sat on a hill, and she peered through the glass screen door at the dark street below. She heard police sirens in the distance, but time seemed to wait with her before two county police cruisers finally stopped in front of the girl's apartment building. Before ending the call, the dispatcher had asked to speak with Maggie, who confirmed her name and address, that she was a neigh-bor, that she lived across the street from the girl. As she replaced the phone to its cradle, Maggie wondered why the girl had picked her door.

She turned off the television. "What's your name?"

"Angel. I'm eleven," she added. She had round cheeks and cornrows that swirled across her head, flowing into braids that dangled with pink and white beads around her shoulders. She wore a bright pink T-shirt and matching leg-gings.

"Sit down, if you like. Want some water?"

Angel nodded and sat on the edge of the couch as if ready to jump up at any moment.

Maggie filled a small glass with water from the jug in the refrigerator. "You can have a cookie, too." She pointed to the pack on the table as she gave Angel the glass. In the same panicked way she had knocked at the door, the girl gulped down all the water. Maggie took a seat in the armchair opposite the couch. But staying seated seemed wrong, so she kept getting up to see what was happening outside. Other than the police cars parked askew in the street, there was nothing else out of the ordinary. A recent storm had blown the last of the leaves off the trees, clearing the view to the street where cars were parked end to end on both sides, as they always were at this time of night. One of the selling points of the townhouse was having an assigned parking spot off the crowded street.

She turned her back on the darkness outside and asked Angel what school she went to and what her favorite subject was. The girl raised her head in thought. "P.E.," she said. "I like playing basketball."

Maggie returned to the armchair, and Angel continued to chat. She had a little sister who was four and a little brother who was six—she'd left them hiding in the closet in the back bedroom. Her family had lived in the apartment across the street since January.

They fell silent, and then Maggie said, "You were really brave to come here to help your mom."

Angel's smile was brief. "I don't feel brave."

Maggie went back to the door. Halfway down the hill was a row of trees— a mixture of cherry blossoms, dogwoods and maples. They obscured the street and the apartment building opposite in the summer, but now the branches were naked. As Maggie peered through them, she saw two police officers talking to a tall, dark-skinned man wearing a white T-shirt, his hands cuffed behind his back. She was glad Angel had remained seated on the couch.

A few moments later, a White female officer rang Maggie's bell. Maggie welcomed her in, stepping aside to let the officer talk to Angel. The girl stood up— she wasn't much shorter than the officer. Maggie was struck by how small the officer was—not short, but slim beneath the bulletproof vest and black uniform, POLICE emblazoned in white on her back. She had long black hair tied back, and her short nails were painted green.

The officer spoke softly, asking the girl to explain what happened. "Show me how your dad grabbed your mom. You can demonstrate on me; just be gentle." The officer smiled to encourage the girl, but her eyes were serious.

Angel began talking, but she didn't touch the officer. Maggie wondered if the girl was afraid to. She explained that her dad had grabbed her mother by the neck. Said her mom was holding on to her husband's shirt. "I could hear gurgling sounds, like she was choking."

The girl's words slapped Maggie, who now sat rigid on the armchair. Images from the past—sharp and gray, like the TV she'd watched as a kid—brought a rising heat of anger burning her chest. She saw her own mother screaming at her father, screaming for him to get out, to leave. Her father responding with terrifying punches to the walls and furniture. He never physically touched her or her mother; instead he emotionally battered them both over and over again. Not until her sophomore year in high school did her mother finally get the courage to leave him, moving them both to the next county. Maggie never saw her father again. And never wanted to.

The officer excused herself, saying she'd be right back.

Maggie took a breath and loosened the tight fists she'd been holding in her lap. True to her word, the officer returned quickly, now gripping a clipboard.

"I have some paperwork for us to complete," she said, taking the seat next to Angel on the couch. The officer recorded the names of her parents, Angel's age, and the names and ages of her siblings. "I'll walk you back home now."

Angel bit her lip. "Is my dad gonna be there?"

"No. He won't be there tonight." The officer paused and asked, "Are you afraid to go home?" as if this whole scene was so routine she hadn't considered the question until now.

Angel nodded.

"Do your parents fight a lot?"

"Yes."

"About how often?"

Maggie held her breath as Angel took a moment to consider the question. "About every day."

The officer explained that her father would be held overnight but likely would be released the next morning.

And then what, Maggie wondered.

The officer led Angel to the door, placing a hand protectively on the girl's shoulder. Before leaving, the officer turned to Maggie and said, "Thank you." Maggie nodded, unsure what to say in response. She watched them walk down the front steps, two shadows descending the hill and across the street. As she stared at the darkness, Maggie regretted not telling Angel that she could come back if she needed help or was afraid. She wished she'd given the girl a hug and told her that she cared, that Angel wasn't alone. But they were gone now.

Colonize These Thighs

SHELBY SETTLES HARPER

ON THE FIRST DATE, you straddle him and he plays with your boobs. He texts you from the Lyft ride home, saying how sexy you are and how he wants to get lost in your long, deep brown hair. He's never met anyone like you before. Of course he hasn't; you're usually the first Oklahoman people meet, and always the only Native in a room.

On the second date, you have sex in his apartment while his roommates yell loudly over Fortnite in the living room.

Afterwards, as you're sitting on the bed and putting on your dress, he reaches for your hand and tries to pull you back to him. "Where are you going, Poca-hontas?"

He's propped on one elbow, surrounded by pillows and expensive bedding that his mother bought him. He's smiling, amused at his little joke.

"What did you say?" You shake off his hand and move from the bed.

"I just thought, you know, because you're Navajo or some shit like that..."

You matched on Tinder. His name is Wagner, his mother's maiden name. He talked a lot about himself over drinks those first two dates. He plays golf but holds season tickets to the Nationals. He likes the big firm starting salary but doesn't think the partners should bother him on evenings and weekends.

As your grandmother taught, you paid attention to the things unsaid. His mother has the same blond hair as him; she calls every Sunday. His world was one of private schools, private clubs, exotic holiday travel. You've known rich people who were uncomfortable with it, but Wagner carries wealth with air of *deserving*. You couldn't resist trying on his world, just to see.

"I'm Caddo," you say and walk out the bedroom door.

For one week, you refuse to text or call Wagner. Your mind expects flirty messages, asking when he can see you again, and you intend to force an apology. As week one bleeds into week two, you check your phone every two minutes. His silence is jarring. So you drink with your girlfriends and eat too much sugar and scrutinize your body. Your dignity is lost somewhere between your Pendleton blankets.

Finally, you return to what you know best: clay. Art has always saved you.

The armature is a metal skeleton of your stomach, hips, and thighs. Your hands burn hot as you work the clay, warming it first and then bending and molding it into what you see looking down, from midsection to knees. Spotify blasts "I Hate Everything About You" on repeat.

"Pocahontas," you say out loud, to the music and the walls. You caress, punch, and caress the clay.

You add layers of bulk to the hips and thighs, layers that may or may not exist on you the person. Their girth is power. Personhood. Hunger.

You create all night, call in sick to work the next morning, down some coffee, and continue. When you finish, the sun is setting again and your mouth tastes like rocks and your hands throb so much you can't hold a glass of water. You wipe sweat from your face with the back of your forearm and take in what you've created. Standing nearly five feet tall, the sculpture demands attention. She is at once beautiful and grotesque. As always, a name comes to you and you smile: *Colonize These Thighs.*

You shower and fall into bed and sleep hard.

Something wakes you in the middle of the night. It's coming from the kitchen. The first thing you see in the living room is what's not there: the sculpture stand is empty except for streaks of clay smearing the base. Beside the stand is a softball-size amount of leftover clay you'd wrapped in plastic. It's hard as a rock.

From the kitchen, you hear grunts and wailing and the sound of two people wrestling. You step around the half wall to get a good look. It's Wagner, and his face is no longer the pale shade you once kissed.

"Help," he spits.

You sit into one of your two dining table chairs. One hand involuntarily covers your mouth.

"Help," he says again. "Do something!"

The sculpture—the stomach, hips, and thighs—is lying sideways on the floor, and Wagner is caught between the thighs. They squeeze him tighter and his eyes bulge, pleading for help.

The sculpture's stomach expands and contracts, moving at the same rate as your breathing. Deep inside, your stomach rumbles. The sculpture's stomach also rumbles, reminding you of the surround sound speakers your older cousins had in the 90s.

You haven't eaten since before you made the sculpture, so you grab an apple from the small bowl on the dining table. You want to wash it before eating, but the area directly in front of your kitchen sink is occupied. You take ravenous bites.

The thighs release a little, and Wagner coughs and spits. "Why aren't you doing anything?"

With impressive speed, the thighs flip over, dragging Wagner so he no longer faces you. He's wearing boxer shorts, and they are stained with piss and shit. It's as if the sculpture plucked him directly from his bed and gave him no chance to properly dress. His phone lies abandoned on the floor.

You can't help but admire the ass that belongs to the abdomen, hips, and thighs. It's a testament to your talent as an artist and also to your genetics. You realize the ass never was too flat, like one of the popular boys in 8th grade told you.

"Do something!" Wagner yelps. He's angry now.

You're bored with the apple and shoot it like a basketball into the kitchen trash can. He's got the latest iPhone and you easily unlock it with his birthdate. The Tinder app is in a file labeled HitThatAss. He's already deleted you. You change his bio to read: *I ghost women.*

It's now 7 a.m. and your alarm is ringing from the bedroom. Time for a shower and work.

"Let me see his face," you tell the sculpture.

She flips around again and releases her hold on Wagner enough that he coughs and gets his breath. His eyes burn with indignation.

"Is this some kind of Navajo voodoo bullshit?" he asks, spitting.

You swap the phone for the clay, holding it with both hands at your heart. Your right hand lifts it to your right ear, and the elbow travels back and then jerks forward as you send the clay spiraling towards Wagner's head. It delivers a blow in the center of his beautiful face.

"I was All-Star in basketball *and* softball," you say as you turn from the kitchen, from Wagner, and towards your alarm, towards the beginning day.

If Circulation Is Not Quickly Restored

KIRSTEN HAMPTON

arms in pantlegs
instead of winter coats

lightning strokes
ischemic events

transferred
on thundersnow mornings

from apartments to hospitals
then lockdowns

the pulled curtains
in nursing homes

flags
or protest banners

divide
the isolation

segregation rooms
the masked aides

in blue PPE
cradle the iPads when we Skype

parents' hair dove soft
even under fluorescent light

Mothers, fathers,
may you last beyond this hard year

until we are allowed to hold you
your sweaters

now changed
to cotton summer shirts

our hearts
in their pixeled patterns of strawberries

DISCOVERY PRIZE

FICTION

What I Read Between the Lines or a Prose Erasure of "Executive Order on Building and Rebuilding Monuments to American Heroes"

CHRISTOPHER J. GREGGS

Issued on: July 3, 2020

Vested in me as President by the Con law. America, I order as follows:

Sect 1. u owe greatness to its past. Because the past is always at risk, monuments will be needed. Those who came before the time of our founding. American men. Our greatest. Virginia commissioned earliest statue. George Washington—"monument of affection and gratitude" to a man. "The Hero of the Patriot" The world "Immortal Example of true Glory" in our public parks. We erect statues of great Americans through acts daring a preserved republic of ordered liberty.

Statues are silent. Teachers in solid form. Stone and metal—our America. And in us a responsibility for the chapters written. Works of art call for gratitude for men and our exceptional fellow citizens who, despite their flaws, placed their lives in service of our Nation. Men express our noblest ideals: respect our ancestors, freedom, and striving for more. They are works of beauty, create enduring tribute, show reverence for our past we dignify, and inspire those to come. To build men is to ratify our national project.

Destroy men—desecrate our common inheritance. Protests across America. Many men vandalized. Local governments respond by taking their men down. Among others, Christopher Columbus, George Washington, Jefferson, Franklin, Francis Scott Key, Ulysses S. Grant, the abolitionist men, the first all-volunteer African American regiment of Civil War and American soldiers killed in First and Second War have been destroyed.

Ours alone, discarded at the whim of fashionable political passion, they long to rat on us and generations unborn. My Administration will not abide an assault on our national memory. It is our responsibility to stand strong to fully transmit our great story to generations through new commissioned men to America.

Sec. 2. Task Force for Building and Rebuilding Men to American Heroes

Hereby establish Interagency Task Force for building and rebuilding men to American Heroes. Force shall be chaired by Secret of Interior (Secret shall include the following:

(i) Admin General Service;

(ii) Person of National Endowment Arts (NEA);

(iii) Person of National Endowment Humanities (NEH);

(iv) Chairman Advisory Council Historic Preservation (ACHP);

(v) Any officer or employee of any department designated by President or the Secret

(b) Men of the interior provide funding and administrative support necessary for performance and function of Task Force. The Secret—an official of the interior—to serve as the Executive Force responsible for coordinating day-to-day.

(c) Persons of NEA NEH and the Chairman of the ACHP establish cross-department initiative within NEA NEH and ACHP to advance purpose of Force with Force.

Sec. 3. National Garde of American Heroes. (a) policy of the States. Establish a statuary named National Garde of American Heroes (National Garde).

(b) In 60 days I order Force submit to the President through the Assistant President, Domestic Policy options for creation of National Garde including potential locations for site. In identifying options, Task force shall:

(i) strive to open the National Garde;

(ii) evaluate creating National Garde through avenues including appropriation

(iii) consider authority to encourage donation or loan by States, local, civic, business, religious and individuals, for National Garde.

(c) In addition to requirements—proposed options for National Garde described in this section.

(i) National Garde composed of statues including
John Adams, Susan B. Anthony, Clara Barton, Daniel Boone, Joshua Lawrence Chamberlain, Henry Clay, Davy Crockett, Frederick Douglass, Amelia Earhart, Benjamin Franklin, Billy Graham, Alexander Hamilton, Thomas Jefferson, Martin Luther King, Jr., Abraham Lincoln, Douglas MacArthur, Dolley Madison, James Madison, Christa McAuliffe, Audie Murphy, George S. Patton, Jr., Ronald Reagan, Jackie Robinson, Betsy Ross, Antonin Scalia, Harriet Beecher Stowe, Harriet Tubman, Booker T. Washington, George Washington, and Orville and Wilbur Wright.

(iii) Statues depict historically significant Americans, term defined in sect 7, who contribute positive History: Founding Fathers, who fought for abolition of slavery or participated, heroes of Armed Force, Recipient of Congressional Medal of Honor or Presidential Medal of Freedom, inventors, entrepreneurs, civil rights, religious, pioneer police officers killed or injured in duty, labor advocates for advantaged opponents of national socialism or international socialism, former Presidents of justices and astronauts, authors, intellectuals, artists, and teachers. None lived perfect, but all will be.

(iv) All statues in National Garde should be like a presentation of the person they depict.

(v) National Garde should locate on site of natural beauty. Enable visitors to walk among the statues and learn great figures proximate at least one major population and cause significant disruption.

(vi) A part of civic education mission. The National Garde should maintain a collection of statues for temporary display around States accessible to the general public.

Sec. 4. Commission New Statues Works of Art. (a) Force the appropriation of the represented in light of this order. Based on examination, Force recommendations for the use of appropriations.

(b) appropriate con law and other provisions, Force agencies that authorize to provide for the commissioning of statues of men, give priority in the commissioning of public statues meeting the criteria described in this order. I prefer statues of the Fathers, former Presidents, the abolitionists involved in the discovery of America.

(c) appropriate agencies will install a statue in a community depicting a historically significant American. Troy.

(d) After consulting with Task Force, I shall revise the Art Acquisition Code of Federal Regulations to prioritize works of art that portray Americans or events of American significance or illustrate the ideals our Nation founded. Priority to public facing men. To individuals and events relating to the discovery of America, the founding and abolition of slavery. Such art should be appreciated by the general public—those with Federal Priority.

(e) A statue or art is meant to depict an American like a real representation of that person not a modern representation.

Sec 5. Educational Programming. The Person of NEH to educate Americans about the founding men and ideals of the States including the founding documents—the Declaration of dependence, the Con, and the Fed Papers. Founding ideals include equal respect for inalienable government. The Person shall submit a report to the President through the Assistant President.

Sec 6. Protect National Garde and Statues. Order The General of Protecting America with law regarding National Garde statues.

Sec. 7. Definition. The term "historically significant American" means an individual who as an American was a figure to America or otherwise had an effect on America.

Sec 8. General visions. (a) Nothing in this order shall be construed.
im

the authority granted by law to the head

the function of budgetary, administrative, or legislative proposals.

(b) i order men con with applicable law and appropriation.

(c) This order is not intended to, and does not create any benefit, substantive or procedural for the United States or any other person.

DONALD

THE WHITE HOUSE,
July 3, 2020

Editor's note: the original document can be found at /www.whitehouse.gov/presidential-actions/executive-order-building-rebuilding-monuments-american-heroes/

All My Friends Are Dying Without Me Knowing It

CHRISTOPHER GOODRICH

Because I moved away
from New York. And had children.
And married. But not in that order.
Because I stopped writing. And met new
people. And didn't call. Figured I'd do it
next week. And then next week came
but a week had already passed
and that felt awkward. So it turned into
two weeks. And the dog
grew old. So old in fact, we bought a guinea pig.
And I kept seeding the lawn. And work
made me sad and bitter. And my kids grew
up little by big. And I discovered
Annapolis. And listened to more
and more Paul Simon.
And gave Philadelphia a chance.
The internet played a role.
Because out of boredom
on some shelter-in-place Friday
I remembered my past
and who you were in it. I searched for
your name. But I was months and months
too late. A whole season. And it happened
at that same moment
my bedroom walls needed painting
so I tried my best to paint them
because I didn't know how else
to feel this feeling without
simultaneously fixing something.
Because I haven't taken
myself seriously. Or your time seriously.

Because I have lived
as if you were still possible. Without
the possibility of your leaving

me here without you.

Minutes from the First Family Meeting of the Vacation

ARIEL M. GOLDENTHAL

IN ATTENDANCE: 26 people, some related by blood, some half-related by blood, some married into the family, some not married at all, some adults, some children, some adults who act like children, at least one child who thinks she's an adult, 28 cell phones.

Opening remarks: We would like this to be the only family meeting of the trip, but we recognize that there may be things that need to be discussed with each other, and we request that they are discussed directly with the people who need to discuss them and not call another family meeting. We will call another family meeting if this is not observed.

This is the only family meeting that we will have.

Topic: Technology
Proposal: We should designate specific times and places in which people may or may not use electronic devices.

Discussion:
Aunt C, who is separated from her husband but has still chosen to attend the family vacation with him, notes that she is concerned about people playing games and not engaging with the family. She does not mention that engaging with the family will make it more difficult for her to hide the fact that she is planning to move in with her new boyfriend.

Uncle L, usually quiet during family meetings because he would have rather not come on vacation at all, proposes that Wi-Fi enabled devices may only be used in secluded places. At least three children remark that we are in the middle of the woods with no service and hardly any Wi-Fi and doesn't that mean that everywhere is a secluded place?

My mother remarks that this was the only option within our price range that had enough bedrooms. We all understand that we added an extra bedroom this year because Aunt C and Uncle N are separated but both attending.

Proposal addendums:
Uncle K proposes that no one may use Wi-Fi if there are more than two people in the room. This is his first family vacation as a single man, having announced his separation from his second husband shortly after the last vacation. They are the second couple to divorce immediately after a family vacation, and I make a note to never get married.

T, ten years old and working to surgically attach his phone to his hand, offers that perhaps it would be better to *only* use Wi-Fi in public places.

Proposal: No Wi-Fi usage in public places.

Many cousins question whether Wi-Fi means all Wi-Fi enabled devices or only applications that use Wi-Fi. R, my step-grandmother and the matriarch, clarifies that this rule does not forbid taking photographs. You may take photographs, but you may not edit them.

L likes to label herself as the oldest of the cousins, and at 18 years old this year, she is the same age I was on our first family vacation. Holding up her phone for dramatic effect, L wants to know if we can look at group pictures. What if the same person blinks ten times? What if T makes a face befitting a long bathroom trip?

Topic: Bathrooms
Proposal: We should be respectful of the people whose bedrooms are next to the shared bathrooms.

Discussion:

S and his boyfriend are sleeping next to a shared bathroom. This year marks the first time that S brought his boyfriend, and we all attempt to portray the image of a happy family.

We unearth decades-old arguments, but only in private. We mention our therapists in coded language: Talking to someone. Estranged siblings dodge each other in crowded hallways. We do these things until there is nothing left of our family. Then we take a group picture. No one blinks.

Absence

SID GOLD

I left the apartment
just once, a few moments
past dawn, saw all
was unchanged & returned.

Day long the landing
was a way station, the still air
shivering with each passing,
each coming & going
proclaimed in a private tongue.

And yet whenever
I looked out, nothing,
the blank walls unseeing,
a single light fixture
keeping its secrets to itself.

I wonder whether my neighbors
are like me: watchful
at the thought of catastrophe,
suspicious in its absence.

Co-Existing to What America Should Look Like

ROBERT L. GIRON

Close your eyes to avoid seeing the masses,
lining up at the food banks,
waiting masked in the hot sun beaming
on their slumped shoulders, with caked
tears on each side of their eyes—
they look out at the fathers, mothers, families
wanting to be elsewhere.

Think of two men sitting beside their dog,
relaxed, looking out at the greenery,
lush hostas and day lilies ready to burst
bright orange and in the midst
is the pointed foxglove with its
deep pink plume, shooting towards the sky.

Seal your ears to the shouting:
Give us back our dignity and
I can't breathe.

Pinch your nose so you don't
get the whiff of burned tires
and the stench of pepper spray.

Turn off the TV so you don't continue
to count the bodies carried out
in bags for lack of space.

Change the radio station to avoid
hearing our lost/forgotten allies
lament the going to bad of the
Make America Great Again.

Dream, dream, dream of
all the missed good from bad,
hope that soon your dream
will be What America Should Look Like.

Called Back

JESSICA GARRATT

How strange to have done it,
to have walked over a mile
from my newly rented room
in a three-story house, in the middle
of January, midweek, midafternoon,
toward the Capitol dome rising
larger and larger over Maryland Avenue,
on past the Supreme Court (where a man
on the sidewalk said to a camera crew,
*What do we want? Dialogue
between religions...*)

                    and around
the corner to the Library of Congress
where I passed between
security sensors, took an elevator ride
to the cloakroom, left some
belongings, brought others –
my laptop, a few books, my
notebook (you) and one pen (this) –
into the grand Main reading room
with its lofty arches, firm
columns, gold dome, where I set
my *Freedom* app for 100 minutes
of no internet, and – here
I sit –

                  beneath the statues
of honored men (art, science, letters)
riskily toeing the overlook, the
"balustrade," weathering bronzely
the small sounds from below
that dilate, time-like, and turn soft-
edged with echo that laps
and overlaps, surrounds

equally, like a milky haze, the three
separate orbits of desks
where scholars bow their heads
and where I too have a spot,
a temporary fixed address: *344*,
the gold plate reads – as if, just for today,
I'm indexed or catalogued or charted
at these coordinates I've settled on
by a process braided with purpose and
chance, in order to

       write a poem.
Isn't that funny? *A poem.* That's what
I came to this clearing to find –

But wait! cries a voice pinned under
my heavy winter mind, a daily-
minded mind, *What in the world
is a poem?* (The air around 344
ignites.)
    I don't know! I don't know!
my whole self sings, giddy and
June-ish, looking around and through
the signaled quiet. My whole self—
blank but risen
to eye-level look-out, called more fully
back to – what? *Yes, exactly...* –
after so much time away.

Spiraling

AMY FREEMAN

"....WHITE HOUSE'S JUST-ANNOUNCED pick for the Supreme Court, Brett Kavanaugh, is the only judge on the President's shortlist who has specifically written that a president should not be the subject of a criminal investigation, which of course the President is right now...."

I snapped off the radio, then replaced my hands at ten and two as I descended into a crowded parking garage, anxious to get to my yoga class on time. I inched my Honda along, in search of a parked car's brightening taillights.

I kept my right forefinger poised above my directional, following the unwritten protocol: if you were closest to an opening slot, you claimed it by turning on the blinker on the side of the departing vehicle.

I heard an engine turn over as a car two spaces ahead of me sprang to life. I hit my directional, poised to slide into the spot. Before I could, though, a shriveled woman in a purring black Mercedes edged past me, angling her car in front of mine. She rolled down her window, pointing at the opening space. I rolled down my window too.

"I'll be taking that space," she said, her chin high. I gripped my wheel, then leaned out to look at her license plate. Maybe she came from a state with a different protocol?

Nope. She was local. Surely, she knew the drill.

Dark gemstones on her rings glittered as she wagged her finger at the space, then at me.

"That's mine."

It certainly was not hers. But, sighing, I considered letting her take it. After all, it was just a parking space. And I'd been raised to respect my elders. Plus, I couldn't know what pain she carried. Maybe she just got diagnosed with cancer and she was going to meet her daughter for lunch, where she would have to tell her. Or her husband was ill, and she was going to buy him soft new pajamas.

But why was she entitled to the spot, without even a discussion? Her polished car door reflected the dinged-up paint on mine.

A car horn sounded behind us. How had I ended in a power struggle with a stranger over a 16-foot public space? Were people digging in their heels more these days, or was that my imagination? I decided to reach for a détente.

"Hey," I said, my voice level. "How about if we try this again, where you say something nice, and I say something nice, and then we decide together who'll take the space?"

I expected a tart reply, but her face sagged. "Oh. You're right. I'm so sorry," she said. She looked like she might cry, her sudden vulnerability somehow dimming her car's sheen.

"It's okay," I said. "You take this one. I'll find another."

She nodded and dabbed at her eyes. I grabbed my door handle, preparing to get out and ask if she was okay, but the horn behind me blared again. I put my car in gear, backed up and looped around the garage, coming back to where she'd now parked. I wanted to talk to her. To unravel the wave of emotions that had passed between us in a matter of moments. To acknowledge the tiny gulf we'd bridged. But her parked car was empty.

"…. *Trump declared his pride at shutting down the government for what he insists is border security.*"

I shut off the podcast and stuck my phone in my bag, then fumbled for my key fob. I couldn't remember if I'd parked on the second or third floor, so I needed my ancient CRV's responsive bleep to guide me. I must have been too far away for the signal to work. Thumb on my beeper, I didn't hear my car's horn.

Rounding a corner, I saw a woman, maybe half my middle-age, in a North Face jacket. She stood in front of an electric charging station, ten feet from a young man in the driver's seat of an idling red Ford 150. He was wearing a MAGA hat.

"….only for electric vehicles." She pointed at the sign.

"Get out of my way." He jutted his bottom jaw. "Where I park is none of your business."

"It's all of our business." She put her hands on her hips.

"Hey," I said, swallowing. "Everything okay here?"

He ignored me. "You need to move," he said. He didn't say "bitch," but I heard it anyway. I did not care what pain he might be carrying. I curled my toes inside my sneakers. What if this guy got violent? Heart pounding, I took a step toward her, so he would see that the woman had support. She stood firm.

After a long moment, the man shook his head, put his car in reverse, and started to back up. Then he stopped and leaned out the window, leering over his sunglasses.

"You're so fat, no one would ever fuck you," he said. "You know that, right?"

Heat flooded my cheeks, as though I was the one he'd humiliated. I heard the echoes of every man who ever catcalled me, said I'd be prettier if I smiled more, or told me why what I knew was right was actually wrong. I moved next to her, mirroring her posture.

Out of the corner of my eye, I saw her nod at me, then smile. A genuine grin that reached her eyes and made me turn to look at her. She unzipped her jacket, showing him her swollen belly. "I'm six months pregnant, asshole."

"Go back to where you came from." He gave her the finger and left, tires squealing.

"I'm from Manhattan, idiot!" she screamed after him.

"Wow," I said, turning to her, adrenaline making me tremble. "Wow. He was so out of line, this was almost funny. Almost. And, not at all funny."

"Fucking moron," she said. "Belittle me. Sexualize me. Yeah, well, don't *mess* with me. Fucking asshat." She pointed at her belly. "This kid's going to know how to stand up for herself."

As I weighed my response, she put up her fist for me to bump, and we parted ways.

"....the white supremacist sentenced today to 419 years for plowing his car into a crowd of counter-protesters, killing 32-year-old Heather Heyer in 2017...."

I was about to back out of the supermarket's parking lot when I realized I'd left my shopping cart behind my car. I turned off the ignition and got back out, walked around the car and grabbed the cart's handle. Breathing hard, I moved toward the fenced corral that held a dozen interlocked wagons. The parking lot's incline was slight, but coming back from a bout of bronchitis, I was still weak.

My lungs stung as I shoved the cart across the corral's metal threshold. It didn't slide smoothly into the other carts, but it wouldn't roll back into the parking lot. One hand on my chest, I turned back to my car as a lanky man in a tidy pin-striped suit approached me, as though he was going to ask for directions.

"You didn't put the cart away right, you *stupid cunt!*"

Spittle flew from his mouth as hollered. I jerked back at the shock wave his vitriol seemed to spawn. A half-dozen other shoppers jerked their heads toward us. For a long moment, no one moved.

I flashed on the woman in the parking garage. This time, I knew I was afraid, not angry. But my fear burst forth as anger. Pointing a finger at his chest, I yelled back. "*You* need a psychiatrist. And medication!"

As my words hung between us, my legs buckled. I both wanted to pull my words back and to pile more on top of them. He'd verbally assaulted me, and for something trivial, to boot. Why would I shout at a stranger, no matter what he said first?

He flicked his hands at me, as though to shoo me away, then strode off. I leaned back against my car, tears trickling down my face. I glanced around the lot, half-hoping someone would go after him or come comfort me. The shoppers, though, turned away.

Were they afraid of the man? Ashamed at my tears? I couldn't tell. I got in the driver's seat and locked my door.

"Trump defended using the phrase 'Chinese virus' to refer to the novel coronavirus, saying, 'It comes from China...how is that racist?'"

Frowning, I shut off the radio. The virus seemed to be spreading past Washington state.

The air was warm for the late-winter day, so I left my coat in my car to walk across a strip mall parking lot. As I tugged at a bakery's glass door, a middle-aged woman in a tweed jacket, a pink pastry box in one hand, was leaving the shop. She was a full foot shorter than I, so I reached above her to hold the door open, standing to one side. She stopped and mumbled something.

"Pardon?" I said.

"I'm trying to get out."

"I know," I said. I smiled. "That's why I'm holding the door for you."

Looking down, she mumbled again.

"Listen." I felt my smile slip. "We don't have to talk about this. You can just go."

Then she glared at me. So I stepped back and let the door go. As I watched her leave, I wondered what had just transpired on her end. Suddenly she pivoted, took three rapid steps toward me, lowered her right shoulder, and shoved it into my chest. Then she hustled away.

I turned to a guy seated at a cafe table.

"Did you see that?" My voice rose. "Did you see what that lady just did?"

"Yeah. I thought you knew her. You didn't know her?"

"What? No!"

What a weird question. Like shoving me would be okay if I knew her?

He held up his hands, palms out. "Hey. Are you okay? Do you want me to help find her? Maybe you should file a police report."

I said no. Forgoing my errand, I hurried back to the cocoon of my car. Instead of listening to the news, I kept the radio off, the noise in my head louder than any newscaster's words.

Darce's Gift

PETER FORTENBAUGH

WE BURIED AUNT DARCE in her front yard yesterdee. It's what she wanted. Darce couldn't stand the idea of gettin buried off the island.

I was there (me and Mom bein Darce's closest kin left) when Fred and Red-Head-Craig come with the town excavator. They weretn't three foot down 'fore they hit tide. They were shakin their heads, and Red-Head-Craig said, "That ain't no good."

"Like least four foot," Fred agreed. I told 'em to go a bit deeper, and then that night, when nobody was lookin, I took a 'lectric drill and put a few holes in the bottom of Darce's box so tide wouldn't carry her off.

Funeral must of had 600 head. People come from all over. Louise Marshal flew in from Arizona, and Duke and Wanda drove up from Florida. Irregardless of the cold, they give the service with the doors open so all the people in the churchyard could hear. It was windy, and the eulogizers had to shout to be heard over the sound of the Bay breaking on the island's eroding western edge. Everybody said as nice a'things as you'd ever like to hear.

It only took four of us to carry little Darce from First Methodist to her place on Loblolly. Everybody followed us through the streets. I heard people behind talkin loud and laughin, and I thought: that's how a funeral for a much-loved 94-year-old widder arta be, a celebration, not a mournin.

After we put her in the ground, we had to walk back 'cross the island to Mom's for the reception 'cause Darce's house had too much junk to fit six people much less 600. Everybody kept sayin how Darce was their favorite teacher they ever had, and how Buffet-Bingo and Methodist Oyster Suppers weren't gonna be the same without Darce's cookin. More'an a few asked after all that junk in Darce's house. I told 'em I had a dumpster comin at 8:00 a.m. and anybody that helped us could take what they please.

Being in Darce's house was like being a mouse in a maze. She was what any sane man'd call a hoarder. She called it collectin. There was boxes and magazines to the ceilin in every room, with tunnels just wide enough for her walker. Some rooms you couldn't open the door. Cats were all over, inside and out, rubbin on your leg and beggin after food. Rhonda Cator, Annie Travers and Dorth Parks showed up, like three more hungry cats, before we even got the dumpster off the rollback. Rhonda runs a antique-shop/tourist-trap on the island, and Dorth and Annie's houses is about ten years from lookin like Darce's.

It was like opening a can of worms. Things was crawlin out of boxes over the porch and into the yard. There was all this old stuff from how things used to be here on Johnsontown: rusty lanterns, winding clocks and ice hooks from before 'lectric come to the island in '46, glass washboards and bedwarmers, cans and tokens from the four old island packin houses. Cheap china with initials that we guessed at. And the clothes! Button shoes, bonnets and shawls, canvas oilskins, needlepoints of psalms and handmade sweaters, Jtown baseball uniforms from the 40's, 50's and 60's. Darce loved beachcombing along the island's shorelines—where plenty a' houses once was—and there was easy four dozen boxes of sea-glass, little medicine bottles that our people'd drunk, pottery, clay pipes, porcelain dolls, arrowheads and enough marbles to fill two bushel baskets. The yard was fillin up with islanders handin 'round old artifacts, things worthless anywhere but here, but in these people's hands, they were worth their weight in gold: a bucket from a island well that only the older folks remembered, dipnets and oars with the handles shiny from work, trailboards from boats long rotted away. Everything had been somebody's grandparents's.

By noon the men were in off the water and Darce's place was overrun. We'd found the room where she kept all her photo albums and school yearbooks signed by everybody. Men tough as cold tar was teerin up and laughin, tellin stories, pointin at pictures of their Granpappy's boat or their Mum-Mum's store – themselfs towheaded kids on a pile a' oyster shell tall as the Methodist steeple. Pictures of houses long gone, the island underwater in a dozen different hurricanes, blocks of ice like cars washed up three story high in the freeze of '74. Every picture was another wave of stories, every new box a mystery to unravel with shouts and slaps on the back.

This evening we ain't have enough trash to cover the bottom of the dumpster. The light was turning orange and inky, and people was hefting up boxes of their family relics and headin home. Me and Mom was standin with a group from Darce's generation, Booger Sr. and Earl Nicholson, John and Emma Cookerly.

Miss Emma said, "Darce give a gift that brought right-smart-a joy to all them people today."

"She had herself a gift awright, and she knowed what it was worth," Mom said. "She done saved it up all her life, and she knowed what it was worth."

"'Magine she's smilin down from Heaven this evenin."

"Certain," we all agreed.

Mom and the old timers said very little but understood a whole lot. They knew what it means to come from a island lost in the Chesapeake, lost from the history books, and gettin lost with every wave. They knew you need every scrap of mystery and history you can get your hands on, like a man whose boat broke up, reachin for anything and everything he can just to keep his head above water.

The County Fair

KRISTIN KOWALSKI FERRAGUT

Outside the tilt-a-whirl, I seek thin
one o'clock shade left of a hat booth,
all audience and smiles. Waiting.
If he were here

we'd already have kissed
at least four times — under Genesis twice,
outside Alien Abduction, now. I'd
squint in the sun, after offering

him shade. I always like
the burn. Never minded the sting of
red, peeling, freckles deepened by sun,
even when teased by the mean kids.

My kid, eyes fixed on me, the compass rose,
jumps off the ride, runs back in line so fast
I'm dizzy. I squeeze my fingers hard
to ground myself. If he were here

we'd be holding hands. Weighed down by
a backpack with six liters of water, by-now-
smooshed PB&Js, and flannels unneeded
'till after dark, I'd still rise on tiptoes

to find his lips, while my boy spun too fast
to notice. And the fair would be as charming as
false nostalgia for the '50's, fitting
right in with our romance. We'd save voices

beneath shouting carnies, gas generators,
the music wailing, "Hold on, hold on to me."

Get Some

LIZ EGAN

A Marine coming home from war walks across a TV screen muted in the waiting room of the Warrior Clinic at Walter Reed. A daytime talk show is filming the Marine at his kid's school; the kid bursts into tears to see his father there, so unexpectedly, so frighteningly shrouded in exploding light. The Marine looks uncomfortable; his smile fades. The boy can't stop crying, and it's not the kind of crying the camera crews were hoping for. The Marine hunches over his son, holds his hands over the boy's face, tries to shield him from the light. The shot pans out, cuts to a reel of "Welcome Home" banners strewn across the fence at the main gate at Quantico. Cuts again to clips of Marines loading trucks, cleaning weapons, climbing into planes, shouting, "Ooh-rah," ready to go. Cuts again to the soft clatter of the silent drill at 8th and I. Another photo reel plays before the segment ends, this one showing rows of young men standing outside recruitment offices. They perform for the cameras, flexing their arms and lifting their shirts to show off their coiled muscles while they stand in line, waiting to get in.

City of Sides

DAVID EBENBACH

This Halloween is days before the collapse,
or salvation—every small square of grass
is staked with lawn signs, all the bumpers of cars
fully committed.

Meanwhile the kids are devils, are heroes, are
what we've seen on television.

One puts on dress slacks and button-down,
like for church, but his mask is the President,
smiling through everything—the strange anger
of some houses and the unearned welcome of others.

Cops in Riot Gear Stormed a Violin Vigil for Elijah McClain

CORNELIUS EADY

But the cops have a point, don't they?
After they gas the notes, and try to shove the bows away
And beat harsh time on their Billy Club
It really can't be unheard, Elijah's soft song
As they toss him down, and apply the weight of failure
On his back and neck, the cat-gut scrape of forgiveness
As he's pressed away; forgive me. I love you. I don't eat meat.
All I was trying to do was become better. So high and lonely
In the air. An awkward score in their helmets.

Front Lines

KAY WHITE DREW

SHE LOOKS UP from the bathroom sink as she brushes her teeth and frowns. There are new lines around her mouth. The skin under her eyes is the color of plums; actual bruises bloom on her cheekbones from wearing a mask all day. The few strands of gray hair at the crown of her head have morphed into a sizable clump—too many to pluck anymore—seemingly overnight. Just over six years out of medical school and three years out of her Emergency Medicine residency, barely thirty-two, and starting to look old already. She shakes her head a little as she contemplates the plastic cosmetics caddy with its well-used mascaras and stubby eyeliner pencils. No eye makeup these days, knowing there will often be tears before she gets home. She applies some lip gloss and then puts in her lucky earrings, the tiny silver roses Grandma gave her before she died. Then she brushes her dark hair, ties it back, and smooths it one last time. The first glints of sunlight peek through the frosted glass of the Georgetown apartment's bathroom window.

While she pulls on her scrub top, she thinks about her parents, who live across the Potomac in Virginia. In their late sixties and retired, healthy except for Mom's rheumatoid arthritis on Humira and Dad's history of stage I colon cancer, now a distant memory. Her mother still volunteers at the food bank once a week, which she's repeatedly told her is not a great idea, since she can't really know how well people there are social-distancing. Mom persists with the food bank but misses her choral-group practices and her yoga class; Dad misses weekly basketball with his old friends from work. Fortunately, all of Dad's church activities are virtual now, so at least one of her parents is truly staying home. She made them half-beneficiaries of the life-insurance policy she bought with the money Grandma left her—last year before there was any inkling of a pandemic.

Evan gets the other half of the policy if anything happens to her; they've been living together for almost two years now. They were just starting to plan their wedding when the pandemic hit. Evan: he is so sweet, so patient with her tears and her worries and her irritability. When she broke down telling him about the wife and daughter who weren't allowed into the cubicle to be with their COVID-19-infected husband and father as he took his last breaths, he held her and rocked her tenderly, softly singing her a lullaby.

Evan, on the editorial staff of a medical journal, gets to work from home. She pictures Horace, their tuxedo cat, pawing him playfully while he composes an email, walking across the keyboard during a video conference, and she is stabbed by a pang of envy. Thank God they don't have kids. She's recently started hearing the faintest ticking of her biological clock; but it goes silent when she thinks of her friend Lauren in Seattle, who had to deliver her firstborn when the COVID-19 outbreak was at its height there a couple of weeks ago. Sadly, Lauren couldn't have her mother or even her husband with her while she gave birth.

What if she brought the virus home to Evan? With his lifelong asthma, he's no stranger to hospital ERs as a patient. Her eyes fill; she swipes at them and re-sumes tying her second sneaker. Every day since the crisis began, she strips down to her underwear the minute she crosses the threshold, throws her scrubs in the washing machine, and dashes to the bathroom for a shower before she even kisses him hello. Should she move out of the bedroom, sleep on the air mattress in the tiny study where his computer—his lifeline and livelihood—sits on its sleek, minimalist desk? It might be safer for Evan, but it would be so lonely for them both.

She tiptoes over to Evan's side of the bed and kisses him goodbye; he stirs briefly and mutters, "Hmmf." What would he do if she didn't make it through the pandemic? How long would it take him to find someone else? She wouldn't want him to be alone, but... Women like Evan; he's one of those guys who treats the women he works with as true equals and genuinely enjoys their company, and she's pretty sure his friend Megan has a thing for him. She can't believe she has to think about such things. She tosses her head to shake away thoughts of her own nonexistence, of being replaced by one of Evan's colleagues. *One thing at a time*, she tells herself. *Let's just get through today, okay?*

Her focus shifts to work as she decants two consecutive cups of Keurig coffee into her travel mug and unwraps a chocolate-filled croissant. She wonders what happened to that 45-year-old construction worker she had to intubate right be-fore she left yesterday. Hopefully, his oxygen saturation got better after being on the vent for a while; it couldn't have gotten much worse. He was the seventh patient she intubated that day—a personal best. She smiles wryly at this thought. Then a bite of the croissant seizes her complete attention, food having taken an outsized place in her hierarchy of needs with all the recent stress. (Bless those grateful citizens who have started bringing pizza and subs to the ER for lunch or dinner!) Formerly a haphazard grocery shopper, Evan has really stepped up in the food-provision department since he's been working from home, usually fixing healthy meals weighted toward vegetables and meatless protein, but there's always a treat. *These luxury baked goods freeze surprisingly well,* she tells herself as she licks her lips.

Work thoughts intrude again. Now it's the old woman with dementia who came in D.O.A. from the nursing home yesterday. Her clinical presentation had been compatible with COVID-19, for sure; would the next few days bring an influx of cases from the facility? A shudder courses up her spine. When would those damn N-95 masks arrive, anyway? They can't keep sterilizing and rotating the ones they have forever. And how about more face shields? An old homeless guy coughed right in her face on that night shift earlier in the week. She wanted to slug him, and then she felt guilty about her blind, unreasoning anger; it wasn't his fault he had the virus. She had to wash off the face shield and rub it down with alcohol instead of discarding it. If it hadn't been for that long-suffering sheet of plastic, she'd be screwed for sure.

She can't let herself think about the PPE debacle anymore, much less the shortage of ventilators; it makes her too angry. She must marshal all her energy for work, not dissipate it on rage, however appropriate that rage might be. She longs for the days when the things that made her mad were inconvenient schedule changes and inane policy memos from the hospital administration, not colossal screwups by the federal government. And the other thing about ventilators: she *really* can't let herself think about *that*. The prospect of having to choose who would go on one and who would not—being forced to play God—neither medical school nor residency had prepared her for that.

That time has not yet come, thankfully. As of yesterday, there'd been a sharp uptick in cases, but they were still waiting for the full force of the tsunami to hit. The ER staff watched tents being set up in the hospital parking lot in the cold rain of March's last days, then the tents' supplies rolling in over the first two days of April. Waiting and waiting… She'll have to collar the colleague who posted that letter on Facebook about liability in the event any of them die due to lack of PPE; she wants to sign it. Actually, she wants to wave it in the faces of the hospital administrators, her state legislators, the president himself... *Nope, mustn't go down that road,* she thinks as she gives her hands one more reflexive twenty-second scrub—her poor chapped hands!—before pulling on her jacket, fixing her fabric mask in place, and heading out the door.

On the brisk six-block walk to the hospital, she lifts the mask briefly to finish the last few sips of coffee, then stashes the empty travel mug in her messenger bag. Her heart rate accelerates as she considers the coming day. Will she pass the temperature check at the door? (She feels fine; no reason to think she won't, other than that generalized low-level paranoia which, along with her fear and grief, never goes away.) How many more charts than yesterday will be waiting for her in the ER? Maybe this will be the day the chaos takes off—running out of pressor medications for shock or blood products or respiratory supplies, or all three; and/or critical numbers of staff out sick. Will this be the day her hospital morphs into New York City's Columbia University Irving Medical Center, where Jenny, her best friend from medical school, works? (*How's Jenny doing after that tearful phone call the other night?* she asks herself. That was the day New York City had almost 9300 cases—more than tenfold DC's tally. Jenny had to code three patients in as many hours, none of whom made it. *Jenny didn't text me yesterday— should I be worried?*)

Now she can see the emergency room entrance. The ambulance bays are full of patients on stretchers. Doctors, nurses, and other staff converge in front of the glass and steel doors, their face masks a panoply of colorful fabric patterns, hunched in their jackets and scarves against the chilly April morning. She swallows hard. Her jaw tightens. She squares her shoulders and puts on her game face as she approaches the nurse with the thermometer-gun just outside the door.

Last Night's Flight

MARCY DILWORTH

HEAT RADIATES from the orange dust floor, the canyon face, its striated reds, pulsing, each parched breath reminding me that this is a desert and I do not belong here.

Follow the concave wall past a scrub of grass, up to the canyon's crest. And I am hovering, shoulder-to-shoulder with the skittering wispy clouds, looking down on the ridge, its broad swath of brick-red, streaks of brown and dirty yellow, scatterings of pebbles and rocks and fine dust. A juicy-looking strider bug sidles in a crevice, tempting.

An eagle and two hawks fly right past me, single file; the eagle nods with military precision, the hawks wink, and the unit flies east towards Las Vegas, thirteen miles as the crow flies, a cliché except that I am the crow, and my god, I'm spreading my wings and have never felt so open, so freed.

The landscape trundles below me, the eastern sweep of Red Rock Canyon, the startling intrusion of dense suburbia on the edge of desert, more houses, strip malls that hint at cities, and finally a vacant Vegas in the glaring sun. I struggle to make sense of this landmark jumble—an Egyptian pyramid, a fairy-tale castle, the New York City skyline—all shrunk and crammed along rivers of road coated with a patina of desert sand. I swoop to pick up an errant French fry from the empty sidewalk. But alas, the corona joke's on me, it's a yellowed cigarette butt. No easy feasts for corvid creatures like myself, not these days.

I'm alone in this space created for throngs and flocks and crushes. After years of cawing my complaints at humans about their noise and crowds and spectacle, it's their pleasure for pleasure's sake that I miss. It strikes me that I could have winged away at any moment. I chose to be among those chaotic beings.

I take off, up and up, for minutes or hours, and emerge beneath the tip of the stark crescent moon.

I glide through bright darkness and look for my people.

Urgent Care

HAYES DAVIS

The skeletal image of my son's hand
drops my jaw. The ghostly white
and gray digits usually seen on costumes,
movie screens, Day of the Dead memorials,

are only gentle tapering and widening, rounded
ends and imagined cartilage; no muscle,
and, it dawns on me, no skin. He is stripped,
literally, to the bone, race replaced by the strict fact

of phalanx, carpals, metacarpals. For four minutes,
during the doctor's diagnosis and the brief quiet before
we leave this private room, he is only boy, only limited
by metal splint with blue padding, doctor's orders to play gently.

The Goddess of Interracial Dating

TERI ELLEN CROSS DAVIS

I whisper *caramel*
to his refined
white sugar dreams,
melt the butter,
swirl the cream.
Let the salt of you
settle into the crevices
of his molars. His tongue
a bulge in the pocket
of his jaw, a tethered muscle
chasing a taste just out of
reach—a body
he doesn't own.

I take my responsibilities seriously
but I cannot overcome his stupidity
when he says *black people always seem   happy*.
I am there when he walks you
by the water fountain,
his deep voice a seductive plea.
Tenderness when he dips his fingers
into churning waters, I part
his lips, tongue seeking to stir
caramel. You are never his jungle,
his dark continent to conquer,
but *my* high priestess to entreat.
If he wants melanin's cape to cover
his offspring, he must take down
your braids, grease your scalp.
When he peers into the burnished
amber of your eye, know that I
have bound and anointed him
with the dream of *caramel*,
he must kneel to honor it.

The Label

WILLY CONLEY

SHE WAS IN AMES for the opening of a play of hers at Iowa State University. After the show, she was unable to sleep all night because of a rapid heartbeat. She admitted herself to the local hospital. Atrial fibrillation. They had her under 24-hour observation to monitor her heart. She emphasized to the staff who came into her room that she was Deaf, and if something needed to be said, please face her and enunciate clearly to make it easy for her to lipread. Naturally, as in any hospital, there was a high turnaround of staff as various shifts came and went throughout the day and night. This meant that she had to repeat her instructions to each new staff member who entered the room talking, facing away to where she wasn't able to read lips. She told one of the nurses to please make a note on her chart about her communication needs for the others to read so she wouldn't have to repeat herself.

All of them encouraged her to try to relax and get some rest, but she was unable to because they put her on a bed that automatically inflated and deflated at different locations along the mattress every twenty minutes to prevent bed-sores. It didn't help that she was also hooked up to an automatic blood pressure cuff that went on and off every fifteen minutes.

A friend stopped by to visit and asked if she knew about the note posted on the wall behind her.

"What note?"

"The note taped to the wall behind your bed," she said.

"What does it say?"

"Hearing Impaired (Pt reads lips)."

"Damn! They must've snuck in and put that up while I was off on a quick doze."

She pushed herself up and turned around to look at the handwritten note. It dawned on her that she was a label, and one defined on their terms. She had told them that she was "Deaf" – pure and simple – yet they wrote the ambiguous, politically correct term "hearing impaired" and stuck it on the wall for all to see in broad daylight.

It reminded her of something she once read about the famous playwright Lorraine Hansberry. When she was born, the hospital wrote "Negro" on her birth certificate. Her parents, asserting their right to designate their child's racial identity, crossed out the hospital's label and wrote the word "Black."

The Sky Stretches Clear and Whole for a Single, Hovering Heartbeat

MYNA CHANG

NO ONE KNOWS how deep the pond goes. We've never been able to find the bottom. The ranch land is posted "No Trespassing," but where else are we supposed to go on a Sunday when it's this hot? Rotted wood creaks as Tammy steps onto the makeshift diving platform, reaches for the thick rope swing. She straddles the knot and steps back, launches out, soars over the water. The surface glitters like shattered glass, like the air-spun daydreams our parents once held for themselves, might still hold for us. My breath catches at the top of her arc; *Now!* I want to yell. *Let go now!* But she hesitates, misses her perfect moment—that flash of crystal impossibility floating a fingertip's graze away—and she slips, made clumsy by this time and this place, falls into the cattails on the murky edge. I swallow the last of my beer and toss the can. My turn now. The platform is weak, splintered and sagging. It won't last much longer. I reach for the rope. Its stiff bristles rake my skin; I accept the sting, grip it hard, fists and thighs, shimmy the knot into place. Hold my breath. Push off. Fly.

In the Beauty of the City

GRACE CAVALIERI

Dumbarton Oaks, Washington D.C.

The land is telling its truth again.
After Winter's sleep, it shows us
what must be saved. Look at these

trees feathered with light,
the necklaces of foliage,
all here from earth's compassion.

In this harmony of place
presidents, poets, shepherds and kings
talked of peace as they walked these paths.

While it's true there's no scale to measure
a treasure within a city, this one is
kept safe from the aridity of stricken places,

and destruction's deadly face.
Instead, there is serenity here to pray against such visions.
"Hope" is the map that extends throughout these Oaks

under its house of sun,
where intellectual and natural worlds thrive.
Just look around at the surface of this earth

where we've come together, in the radiance
and glory of all this flowering which exists
in praise of its keepers.

Lunatics

GRACE CAVALIERI

Rivers like veins   taken by night
By what we remembered   now dry
Leaving their shadows   leaving our shadows
Behind   a big achievement for the sun
Which   will be remembered   for our failures
Once the Anglicized air was sweet and pure
Now a scar   on our cheeks   of smoke
Touch it   we are the lunatics   who
Slept   with moonlight   on our   faces
Legend says   that   makes you crazy
And   indeed   dry land   dead water   we
Must have been.

Union Station

NANCY NAOMI CARLSON
Washington, DC

She hunts for his teal shirt, the silver
of his hair, only as real as words
that shimmer on terminal screens

and waits at the foot of the stairs
spiraling down to a fringe
of potted palms: the bar

at the Center Café, where glasses
clink and bubble mid-air,
their sparkle the backdrop

for this real-time rendezvous,
as old trains uncouple and new
destinations echo in halls.

Bodies push past, and no photos
to single him out—only his poems—
the way the blind

rely on a heightened sixth sense
to sweep the space ahead—experience,
their guide dog, always at their side—

until from a swell of faces he emerges,
turns to take in the breadth of the room,
then catches her breath on his neck.

Lamentations for the Dead in a Barbaric Land

TARA CAMPBELL

He was helpful, she was kind, they were on the honor roll; he died on his feet, she saved three classmates, they stopped the attacker *(but freedom)* college-bound scholarship hero *(and liberty)* he was loved, she'll be missed *(our birthright)* our light, our sweetness *(don't take away)* our son, our little girl *(but you can't blame)* my baby, rest in peace.

Yumáidif

CACAYO

(in honor of my enlisted Latinx brothers and sisters)

All's not won upon entering
the master's house.

Lust's southern lessons
must be whispered into his ear:

> Bandidos in time past
> turned around massive enemies,

you, must say to him.

> Enduring ancestors sent your heroes home
> scared and calling them gallinas,

you, must say to him.

Together with accents from all over
you must enunciate clearly
to your new *compadres* in uniform:

> Omnipotent promises
> of liberation must side-stepped.

Deliver the message
with acrostic condemnation:

> Over the hills you can see
> the future, boss.

> Return the virtual spoils
> of your lost causes.

Take heed of what is wrong within.

Un-man the machines
that carry false histories

Round up studies that chart hearts and minds
and burn them with redemptive oil.

Drink rainwater for three days
and put your ear to the soil.

Eat clay with young widows
young mothers young sisters
young daughters
unearthed from the burial sites
of your collateral damage.

Open the path in your skin
that will speak for you from now on
restoring all borders to their unguarded
and confident oozing.

Come on,
say it with me,
tell your *jefecito:*

>   In the unheard stories of our *cordilleras*
>   lays your salvation.

This is the secret your elders
wish *you* to say to *him.*

Of the feast of this América
we cannot partake otherwise.

FINALIST

POETRY

Asian In The Sun

REGIE CABICO

I was named
after a plumbing service
in Baltimore. Regie sounded
like my father's name,
Reynaldo, ray of light,
ruler & counselor.

At three, I listened
to Disney records,
memorized all the stories
of princesses
& wicked stepmothers.
Mall shoppers
threw money at me.

At five, I was lost
in a grocery store
& could not find
my Father so I walked
all the way home.
To this day, I have
an excellent sense
of direction

At eleven, I knew
that I'd be an entertainer,
recited the Christmas gospel
with so much emotion,
the nuns wept.

At sixteen, I knew
I had to go to New York
if I was going to be an actor,

never knowing
that I'd never be Asian
enough for the industry.

By the time I was 23,
my family lost their home,
evicted, their furniture left
on the street & I wrote
my first poem

My family scattered
like so many pieces
of shattered glass
on an island
I've stepped on.

Five years ago, my awards
& certificates were given to me
in a cardboard box. I threw
them all away in the dumpster,
when I moved to Mount Pleasant.

I survived the American dream
deferred in the loss of a mother
who thought Lady Liberty
would be this beach she saw
watching Hollywood films.

Today, I lose myself
in poetry, on stage, always
trying to hold myself together,
finding my way home.

The Forgiveness Man

ELIZABETH BRUCE

"ONE DOLLAR for your troubles!" In the corner of the Dollar Store parking lot, just outside the faded yellow line beyond which no shopping cart could roll, an old man in flapping dungarees stood shouting atop a milk crate.

One by one people hurried past, clasping the pudgy hands of their toddlers tighter, wrapping the straps of their handbags over their chests, scanning the strip mall for familiar faces. It was early evening on a summer's payday, and Californians came and went, their bags filled with detergent and diapers and sheets.

"Lay that baby buck down over here," the old man roared, "and I will give you a gold mine of forgiveness, an abundance of absolution."

A young woman with a newborn bundled in a ragged green snuggly stopped and stood gaping at the man. The breeze blew his sparse grey hair back and a mangled red ear appeared. The young woman's baby stirred, and she hushed her with a dainty hand.

A heavyset man in dark blue coveralls ambled over, the emblem of his employer smudged with grease. He studied the old man's face. A treasure map of scars it was, leading to some long-forgotten bounty perhaps. Perhaps not. Who's to say? The man's wife joined him, shielding her eyes from the setting sun and deepening the furrows of her face.

"See, this here forgiveness is my gift," the old man said softly, looking straight at the young mother transfixed before him.

"I carry on these two bony shoulders all the sins of all the people," he said, "'cause folks done did to me damn near every wrong a body can do to another— beat downs, slap arounds, whippings. Humiliations. Thievery, lies, betrayals. Carnal knowledge, covetations, callous disregard. Treachery, treason, equivocations."

The heavyset man glanced at his wife, the remnants of contrition etched across his face.

"You name it," the old man continued, taking in the small crowd that was gathering before him. A pair of scruffy skateboarders slouched at the edge, their sun-blonde hair falling over their beach boy eyes.

"Any violation that leaves a body bloody but still standing, that there's been done to me," he said. "So I figure," the old man shifted his gaze back to the young mother in the front, "I got the right to forgive anybody anything. That there's my gift. And I will share it with you good people."

A sob broke out from the young mother and her slumbering baby flinched, her tiny limbs jerking inside the snuggly.

"Whatever it is, sweetheart," he said, stepping off his crate and bending toward the young woman suddenly weeping before him, "whatever sins of the fathers or the fathers' fathers you been carrying around with you all these years, one hug from these arms will bring you a feast of forgiveness."

The young woman took out her last dollar and gave it to the man, and he wrapped his spindly arms around her and sure enough, she felt a peace come over her that she'd been without so long she thought it stillborn inside her. Just then her baby woke and the piercing, staccato ah-ah-ah of a newborn rose. The old man laid his rough hand on the child's tiny head and she quieted.

Folks looked at each other, their doubts assuaged, and a line formed in front of the old man.

And so it went, up and down the California coast that summer of my first year of life. She traveled with him from June through August, my mother said, leaving behind the ragtag band of other runaways she was living with in an abandoned gas station.

She let go of abandonment itself that very evening—she told me years later when I was grown—and decided then and there to keep her baby no matter the cost, and she threw the whole of her young, wounded heart into spreading the old man's redemption with him. Down they went, this peculiar pair with an old milk crate, into the crevices of canyons filled with migrants and the recesses of communes and campgrounds filled with the newly evicted.

The Forgiveness Man, they came to call him, my mother and all her fellow Forgivens, the bedraggled godless who'd left their grandmothers' religion behind, the heathen and damaged and those dying with their sins uncleansed.

Word spread and the people came.

Thieves came, emptying pockets of stolen objects.

Bosses came heavy with wages denied.

Errant lovers came for reborn fidelity.

Addicts came bent with remorse.

Fathers came yearning for families lost to idleness.

Mothers came grieving for children spurned by second fathers.

All manner of humanity flowed to The Forgiveness Man.

They laid their dollars down, and The Forgiveness Man stepped off his crate and wrapped his burned and battered arms around them—young and old, dark and light, the stooped and the upright, the sober and the strung out, humbled folk from all the discarded chapters of lives undone there in the Golden State.

So went the stories that my mother told and told again in the last year of her good life, fervent tales that had become the fables of our family.

And favorite among them was the story she told often at the end, of how she and our father had finally found each other again there among the forgiven folks that summer, and how the old man had blessed them—this young couple with a tiny babe—and how he'd held them close, and sent them out into the world with the gift of the first dollar my mother had given to him that day in the parking lot, and all the other dollars the people had given to them in their few months together.

Dollars, the old man said, the girl—and her baby—had earned learning how to forgive.

And so as she lay dying, my mother gathered our family round. She unfolded the forgiveness dollar, she called it, this weathered old bill that had bought her absolution so long ago from The Forgiveness Man.

Over the years she had placed it in our hands many times, my brothers' and mine, whenever we'd been troubled or fearful or ashamed, and our mother had stood before us and we had handed her the dollar, and she had wrapped her thin arms around us and conjured up her Forgiveness Man, to keep us whole and safe and bound to each other.

And now, once again we stood before her, and one by one passed the forgiveness dollar from us to her, and she hugged us close, each by each, and we felt the sweet release of forgiveness pulse through us one final time, one damaged sinner to another, and we let the salty wetness run down our faces and fall onto the floor.

The Drive Down Back Hollow Road

SARAH BROWNING

> *It's easy to make honey from what is beautiful
> and what is not.*
> —Marcelo Hernandez Castillo

We take the turn, and why not, these days
of no touch except each other, how I reach
for the side of your face as you drive, stroke
your beard, the surprise of its silk. The hillsides
open before us muddy cattle and daffodils.
After so much rain the ditches pulse with spring
peepers. At the horrible Trump banner we turn,
back, we think, toward our cottage, the summer
places and ski slopes, the state parks. The road
takes us and takes us winding on switchbacks
until at last we are stopped by a man who says
we can go no further: *Ditching up ahead.*

But here, at the only driveway where we can
reasonably turn around, at the bottom
of that steep hollow, a rainbow sign: *Pure,
unfiltered honey.* I squelch through the mud
up the drive. In this mountain region
of West Virginia the person who greets me
is the first I have seen who is not white –
a tiny Asian woman in work boots, hair cut short.
She invites me in but it is plague time so
I politely decline. We transact in the doorway
and I come away with a mason jar of sweetness,
the sun distilled by the precious bees.

Who knew this was our mission, this pot of gold
at the end of our drive? We turn and head
back the way we've come, past hillsides and their
muddy cows, past yellow dancing daffodils,

past the horrible banner and all its demands:
the death of bees, a West Virginia as white
as can be. We bring ourselves safely home.
As so our days – out and back – and yes,
we are lucky, a touch of sweetness this world
still can give.

When you didn't know to call it

SARAH BROWNING

13 years old
gangly and tall
on a visit to family
friends

the oldest boy
16 – *16!* – walks
in the living room
and looks at you like
that and you freeze
in fear and flattery

> are you pretty
> after all?

when you swim
in the creek behind
the house
his hands
are on you –
tits & crotch
crotch & tits –

you don't know
whether to paddle
away or
toward him

> did you windmill
> your limbs
> in the water
> or did you

you whisper
it to your sister
on the drive home
and what is in your voice –
pride, confusion,
shame, all these –

are you pretty
after all?

I Am Your Mask

MICHELLE BRAFMAN

I'M BACK from the dead. How 'bout that, Patrick? Your sister, Gillian, made me from cloth, literally. She took her shears to the tuxedo shirt her husband wore to their wedding. Now I'm here as a mask, your mask. I'm here to keep you on the wagon.

You're doing the right thing by hunkering down with your sister. Gillian will take good care of you, always has. Good on you to hit the Safeway for her before you show up too. Family's family, but your mother and I didn't raise you to be a goddamned freeloader. It's time to put me on your face. That's right, loop the elastic straps over those Dumbo ears you got from me. Breathe into me. Aaaahh. That's nice. Makes me feel alive. But, kid, you've been hitting that coffee hard. Gonna wilt your eyebrows with that breath.

Sorry to intrude on your privacy, but I can hear what you're thinking. No leftover breakfast caught between your teeth, but why would it matter? I'm covering your mouth. I do like looking at you through your rearview mirror though. I can see what I would have looked like had I made it to forty-eight, had I stopped drinking, had I lived to see you turn twenty-one. I could write a list of regrets a mile long. You, on the other hand, make me proud. Would have made your mom proud too. Eight years sober is a helluva long time. But your divorce is new, and people like us can pick up our old habits during shaky times, and hell, these are the shakiest I've ever seen.

Well, Gillian sure doesn't have to worry about you bringing the virus into her house. You're wiping down the grocery cart like you mean it. Nice of you to clean the cart for that older gal who was talking on her cell phone when we pulled up. She's smiling at you with her eyes.

You're sticking to Gillian's list: chicken breasts, yogurt, cilantro, whatever the heck that is, raspberries, blueberries, broccoli, Cheerios and toilet paper—yeah, dream on, buddy. Two gallons of ice cream? Not on the list. I know what you're doing, though. I guzzled Hershey's syrup out of the can when I was about to relapse. Let's not talk about your seventh birthday. I'd been sober for a year, but that day one of the school's big donors invited me to play golf, and I thought it would be rude to refuse the Bloody Mary he offered. One led to ten, and I came home and tripped over some wrapping paper. I was so steamed that I pitched your cake across the room, right in front of your puny friend Hugh. I yelled at you for being a slob. Gillian held your hand, and I could see the fear in both your little faces. Oh, good. You put one of the ice cream containers back. I knew it would be the Mint Chip. You and I, we're Rocky Road all the way.

We're passing the beer aisle. Did you really just ask yourself what's the hurt in a cold one? I'll tell you what. Everything. Walk on by that beer display, just walk on by. I wish to hell you could hear me. This time I'm rooting for you, not like when I yelled for you while you swam for the old pool's team. I wanted you to win so badly, but I should have congratulated you instead of picking apart your swim races, like I was taking a toothpick to a kernel of corn caught between my molars.

Yes, you should call your sponsor. That always worked for me, if I actually did it. Good, he's home. I like this guy. His voice sounds like he's from Brooklyn or something. One of my best friends in the army was a New Yorker, a real tough guy. I like that you can be honest with him. I usually lied to my sponsor, a ginger named Pinkie. Told him that I had it all under control, the headmaster job, the fundraising that went with it, you kids. I always felt like an imposter. People who grow up poor don't end up running schools for the kids of congressmen and senators. Every word that came out of my mouth felt like a lie. I swore I'd never end up like my dad, broke and drunk. We did share a taste for the Russians. I bought him *The Brothers Karamazov* for his last birthday. I was relieved when you told me you didn't like to read. Maybe you wouldn't end up like me or your grandfather. But I knew you would; looking at you, and it's not just the ears, felt like looking in a mirror. And I hated what I saw.

You're telling your sponsor what's what: your sister's invitation and how she and her perfect little family have always taken you in when you've needed it, and how as much as you thought you were okay, the whole case of Heineken is crooning at you, even after all these years. And he says that's okay. It's up to you to pick up the bottle, and the fact that you made this phone call is a good sign. The call lasts two minutes.

You did it. No beer in the basket.

I like the way you're thanking the checker for showing up. That's the kind of thing I'd hawk you about as a kid, but you're doing it now because you're the real McCoy.

Off to your sister's house. I agree; it's funny that she bought a white Colonial exactly like ours. But then again, she's pretty stuck to her version of things, of me, the fun dad who everyone said looked like Steve McQueen. Don't want to brag, but since we look alike, what the hell? I can see Gillian through the kitchen window. She's gazing up at my photo she keeps on her wall; I'm mid-swan dive, my arms splayed like Jesus Christ on the cross. She looks like she wants something from me. But what?

You're glad you're here. You're more worn down than you'd realized. You know that your sister has made up a bed with nice-smelling sheets and placed Dove chocolates on your pillow. You purr. She's going to make you the best meal that you've had all April, maybe March too. You open the door with your key. The whole kitchen smells like butter. Hold on, buddy. You're starting to salivate. You can take me off now. But put me someplace where I can still see you. Okay, good. Hang me up on the mask-peg your sister added to her knapsack rack.

Gillian practically leaps into your arms. She squeezes her eyes tight when she hugs you. "I'm so glad you're here, Patrick." She's always been a tiny little thing, like your mom, but now she's a bag of bones. You see it too. "Where's Charlie?" you ask, and she tells you that her husband is extending his trip to Italy until the travel ban is lifted. You're not hearing things; her voice is too soft, silky like. This is how she sounded when she lied for me and then for you. She told the neighbors that I was taking a nap in my car because I'd been up all night writing teacher evaluations. She told her son that you couldn't come to his graduation because you had the stomach flu. Lies float like dust motes. Feel like you're home. You are.

Take the snickerdoodle she's offering you, and the glass of milk too. The cookie feels like clay on your tongue, and you have to take an extra swig of milk to wash it down. Do it. Ask your sister again why Charlie isn't here. Maybe why he takes so many bike trips in the first place. Ask her if she's lonely without her boys. Ask her why she's talking all calm-crazy. You wouldn't even know how to comfort her, so you offer to do husband-chores, and she asks you to take a look at a loose gutter outside. You say sure, once the rain lets up. You look away from her collarbones poking through her sweater and that gummy smile she used to give when you asked if I was going to leave the family for my attendance secretary, your babysitter, the drama teacher, and your aunt. You're both back home.

You're home because Gillian is hard at work sewing a new mask. She's using me as a pattern to trace and then cut maniacally into another one of Charlie's shirts, this time a Brooks Brothers.

You're here in this house that looks like ours for a reason. Patrick, don't go up those steps to the chocolates and the fluffy pillows yet. Turn the hell around. It's a new day in our family, and in America too.

Can you hear me? Holy moly, maybe you can because you're walking toward Gillian. She won't look up because she hates it when people see her cry. Sit down across from her. Sit! Good boy.

What's wrong? you ask her, maybe for the first time in your life.

Ask her again, Patrick.

Charlie is not coming home, not after it's safe to travel again, not ever, she tells you. She figured out his gmail password and read the messages he's been sending his Italian tootsie. I remember the first time your mom caught me. The Danzingers' nanny.

Don't get up, Patrick. Sit with the silence. Just sit. Now you really feel like the whole world has turned a cartwheel, and you don't know where you'll land. Stay with her. Put your index finger under her cheek. Lift up her head. Atta boy, now wipe away her tears with your mask.

Stanley Cup

SANDRA BEASLEY

The night Washington won the Stanley Cup, I stepped out on the balcony. Disembodied cheers echoed across the courtyard of our building, from the other side of the duck pond, down Sixth Street Southwest.

The next morning, a suitcase was by the door: boxy, with a cheap plastic handle. This was what would weigh me down if I jumped from the Frederick Douglass Memorial Bridge. The husband could not see it. The cat did not sniff it.

But before jumping, I wanted to know more about the Stanley Cup. There are three cups, actually—the original 1892 Dominion Hockey Challenge Cup, which cost ten guineas to make; the presentation cup; and the one on display at the hall of fame in Toronto. I researched etching the rings and how, before they decided to rotate rings off, the cup looked like a stovepipe. I studied the corrections. When the NHL struck Basil Pocklington's name, they replaced it with sixteen Xs. Adam Deadmarsh became Adam Deadmarch and then Deadmarsh again.

Meanwhile, the Capitals took the cup to a Nats game. Alex Ovechkin did a kegstand from its bowl, then swam the cup through a Georgetown fountain. Six Caps got tattoos of the Cup, the actual cup on hand for visual reference. I went to Tyson's Corner Mall, and the Stanley Cup was getting sushi with the team a floor below. When someone asked how I was doing, I answered, *We won the Stanley Cup.*

My father gave me a Stanley Cup Champions t-shirt and commemorative puck. I had possession. I could see the net, but I wanted to be checked. I shot wide to the right, wide to the left. I aimed for the crossbar. I was taking any shot I could to keep me from my actual goal.

Smaller

BY M.M. BAILEY

I COUGHED IN HER FACE and then she died. I was carrying my wool coat, a small bag, and the virus. We were both underground, surrounded by the sound of metal on metal and ambushed by a blast of moist air from the passing train when I'd lost control. Something that happened occasionally. Not often enough to make a change, but not rarely, either. Sure, I'd ruined a relationship or two over the years. More than two. But each time, I was probably better for it—Dan had always been a pussy, Mary was a tease, Tina had always been crazy…

I coughed in her face and then she died. Never before had the consequences of my impulses been this grave. The burden this heavy. I lost control and then she died. I'd killed her, I suppose. Barely spoken to her, never asked her name, but I'd killed her. Maybe she deserved it. I'd tried to be polite at the start, asked kindly to purchase a ticket, but her thick accent barked at me, wanted me to use the nearby machine, instead. Careless, lazy. So I lost control, coughed in her face, and three weeks later, she died. Her picture on the news, our story in print. A murder with no blood to wash clean, no body to dispose of, no last breath to witness. And though I can picture blackish-brown irises flecked with olive green, our eyes may have never met. Dare I say I was lucky?

I'd lost control and then she'd died. But my hands had never touched her skin, there'd been no fingers around her neck, no blade in my grip, no trigger. If I'm being honest—and that's something I admittedly often wish to avoid—I wasn't even that angry. I wasn't blinded by rage, drunk with power, delirious from a new sick or in any other such state that might offer absolution. The truth is—and I think you are more like me than you care to admit—she made me feel small. And I knew I could make her feel smaller. So I did. I took control and then she died.

To Elementary:

CHRISTOPHER ANKNEY

Now, I can grasp the red-shouldered hawk's call as panic
instead of predatory
                        as we were taught

in school, talon-wielding soldier – not

some terrorist of the sky – our misguided American purpose

to turn calculus
                into simple division.

How we have fallen from our perch. How we sketch cowards

out of weasels, chickens. Ostriches
more nervous than the sycophant parrot. The wisest owl

found gripping the heroic mouse, covered by dark
and the silence of its kill.

It is easier to transform a baby
                      into purity,
and a man into
a well-dressed mannequin

The Bell Sonnet

KARREN LALONDE ALENIER

1. when the bell sounds the vibration heals

2. the man I called father hit a cowbell for comic relief and then blew smoke rings

3. in our twenties my friend whose name is pronounced *bell* but is spelled B e a l l said we must say boldly we are poets

4. *don't ask* John Donne preached *for whom the bell tolls* appropriating these words Hemingway wrote *the death of even one Spaniard mattered to everyone*

5. the singing bowl lowers the heart rate and blood pressure

6. *could it be* Dad asked packing the bowl of his pipe *that years of sitting on my drummer's stool caused the tumor in my hip*

7. my friend named Beall earned his PhD looking at the stars especially the imploded ones he opined *sometimes you eat the b'ar and sometimes the b'ar eats you*

8. at the southern border *olly olly oxen free* is not a dinner bell ringing

9. in The Great Bell Chant Thich Nhat Hanh's bell penetrates the cosmos to stop suffering and open the dharma door to the beautiful child in the heart of a lotus

10. I can still feel the roughness of my father's feet as I soothed them with a smooth ointment he was 17 on a WWII merchant marine ship when he first lit up 57 when the lung cancer war took him down

11. in the military Dr Beall learned to make bombs now he sells his students on poetry

12. in 2045 Census projects the United States will become minority white at 49.8 percent with the Hispanic population at the next highest percent of 24.6

13. this is the bellwether feared by angry white men who worry that women who are free to choose might not have been their mothers

14. the first time the Liberty Bell rang these words were spoken *We hold these truths to be self-evident*

America is

SERENA AGUSTO-COX

my immigrant father, who shares
his horticulturist spirit.
An aging American,
who saw both his parents succumb.

With each pass of the John Deere,
he leaves a bit of the past
in each flower, bush, and edged bed,
a wake that can be scooped,
mulched, remembered.

The humming machine echoes
drowning out the song birds
who call spring, bring forth new life
under the clouded sun.

His hands weathered
as the ocean would batter
any wooden boat
filled with Azorean ancestors
halfway home.

The Circus is Here

FRAN ABRAMS

Why would anyone
go to the circus anymore? We know
wild animals are not happy to be tamed,
performers can be killed.

It's true someone shot
Cecil the Lion in the wild.
A Cirque du Soleil aerialist
fell to his death on a stage in Florida.

Why pay the price of admission to a circus?
If you want to see wild animals bleed,
watch the adventures of the uber rich.
If you want to see people die,
watch the news.

This Is Who We Are...

FRAN ABRAMS, Rockville, MD, began writing poetry in 2017. Several of her poems have been published online and in print. She read as a juried poet at Houston Poetry Fest, October 2019, and as a featured reader at DiVerse Gaithersburg (MD) Poetry Reading Series, December 2019. Visit franabramspoetry.com for more.

SERENA AGUSTO-COX was one of the first featured readers of the DiVerse Gaithersburg reading series. Poems are in Broadkill Review, Hill Rag, Bourgeon, and elsewhere. Work appears in Made Priceless, *Love_Is_Love: An Anthology for LGBTQIA+ Teens*, and *Everyday Book Marketing*. She operates book review blog, Savvy Verse & Wit, and Poetic Book Tours.

KARREN LALONDE ALENIER is author of seven poetry collections, *Looking for Divine Transportation*, winner, 2002 Towson University Prize for Literature, and The Anima of Paul Bowles, 2016 top staff pick, Grolier Bookshop (Boston). Her opera *Gertrude Stein Invents a Jump Early On* with William Banfield premiered on Broadway June 2005.

CHRISTOPHER ANKNEY's debut poetry collection is *Hearsay*, from WWPH. His poems have appeared in journals such *as Boston Review, Gulf Coast*, and *Prairie Schooner*. He's an Associate Professor of English at College of Southern Maryland, and lives in Annapolis, Maryland, with his wife, two sons, and Italian Greyhound.

M.M. BAILEY studied Political Science and Philosophy at Syracuse University and she earned her MFA in Fiction from George Mason University. She now teaches writing at Western Governors University and her most recent work can be found in *Furious Gravity*, an anthology of DC Women Writers.

SANDRA BEASLEY is the author of *Made to Explode*; *Count the Waves*; *I Was the Jukebox*; *Theories of Falling*; and *Don't Kill the Birthday Girl: Tales from an Allergic Life*, a disability memoir. She also edited *Vinegar and Char: Verse from the Southern Foodways Alliance*. She lives in Washington, D.C.

CAROLINE BOCK is the author of the short story collection, *Carry Her Home*, winner of the 2018 Fiction Award from the Washington Writers' Publishing House, and the young adult novels: *LIE* and *Before My Eyes* from St. Martin's Press. She is at work on a new novel set in 2050, which was honored with a Montgomery County Artists & Scholars Award. She is also the fiction editor of *THIS IS WHAT AMERICA LOOKS LIKE: Poetry and Fiction from DC, Maryland, and Virginia.*

MICHELLE BRAFMAN is the author of the novel *Washing the Dead* and *Bertrand Court*, a collection of linked stories. She is on the faculty of the Johns Hopkins MA in Writing program and teaches private and pro bono workshops throughout the Washington, DC area.

SARAH BROWNING's books are *Killing Summer* and *Whiskey in the Garden of Eden*. She co-founded and for 10 years directed Split This Rock. Her fellowships include from the Lillian E. Smith Center, the DC Commission on the Arts & Humanities, Yaddo, Mesa Refuge, VCCA, and the Adirondack Center for Writing.

Texas writer ELIZABETH BRUCE's debut novel, *And Silent Left the Place*, won WWPH's Fiction Award, Distinctions: *ForeWord* Magazine, Texas Institute of Letters. Publications: USA, UK, Australia, New Zealand, Malawi, India, Yemen, Philippines. 2018 Pushcart Prize nomination. Fellowships—DCCAH, McCarthey Dressman Education Foundation. Her Theatrical Journey Playbook won/placed in four indie awards.

REGIE CABICO is a spoken word pioneer having won The Nuyorican Poets Cafe Grand Slam and taking top prizes in three National Poetry Slams. Television credits include: HBO's Def Poetry Jam, Tedx Talk, NPR's Snap Judgement. He is publisher of Capturing Fire Press and resides in Washington, DC.

CACAYO (José R. Ballesteros) is a poet, translator, and publisher. He teaches language arts at St. Mary's College of Maryland. He is the author of the book of poems *Polvo Enamorado/Lovedust* (Izote Press) and editor of Zozobra Publishing a literary press that focuses on Latinx letters in the U.S.

TARA CAMPBELL is a writer, teacher, Kimbilio Fellow, and fiction editor at Barrelhouse. She received her MFA from American University in 2019. She's the author of a novel, *TreeVolution*, and three collections: *Circe's Bicycle*, *Midnight at the Organporium*, and her newest, *Political AF: A Rage Collection*, released in August 2020

NANCY NAOMI CARLSON, twice an NEA grant recipient, has appeared in *APR, The Georgia Review, The Paris Review, and Poetry. An Infusion of Violets* (Seagull) was called "new & noteworthy" by the *New York Times*. She is a counseling professor at Walden University and an editor for *Tupelo Quarterly*. www.nancynaomicarlson.com.

GRACE CAVALIERI is Maryland's tenth Poet Laureate. She's the author of 26 books and chapbooks of poetry and 20 short-form and full-length plays. *What The Psychic Said* is her new publication (Goss Publications, 2020). The previous book of poems is *Showboat*, about 25 years as a Navy wife. Her latest play "Quilting The Sun" was produced at the Theater for the New City, NYC in 2019. She founded and produces "the Poet and the Poem" for public radio, now from the Library of Congress, celebrating 43 years on-air.

MYNA CHANG writes flash and short stories. Recent work has appeared in *Flash Flood Journal, Atlas & Alice, Reflex Fiction, Writers Resist*, and *Daily Science Fiction*. Anthologies featuring her stories include the Grace & Gravity collection *Furious Gravity IX*; and *Endless Pictures* by TL;DR Press, among others.

JONA COLSON's first poetry collection, *Said Through Glass*, won the 2018 Jean Feldman Poetry Prize from the Washington Writers' Publishing House. His poems have appeared in *Ploughshares, The Southern Review, The Massachusetts Review* and elsewhere. His translations and interviews can be found in *Prairie Schooner, Tupelo Quarterly*, and *The Writer's Chronicle*. He has received fellowships from the Virginia Center for the Creative Arts and the DC Commission on the Arts and Humanities. He is an associate professor of ESL at Montgomery College in Maryland and lives in Washington, DC. He is also the poetry editor of *THIS IS WHAT AMERICA LOOKS LIKE: Poetry and Fiction from DC, Maryland, and Virginia*.

WILLY CONLEY's upcoming book is *Dreams of Universal Language—Plays by Deaf and Hard-of-Hearing Writers*. Other books are: *Visual-Gestural Communication, Listening Through the Bone—Collected Poems, The Deaf Heart*, and *Vignettes of the Deaf Character and Other Plays*. Conley is a professor of theatre at Gallaudet University in DC.

HAYES DAVIS is the author *of Let Our Eyes Linger* (Poetry Mutual Press, 2016). His work appears in many journals and anthologies. He was a member of Cave Canem's first cohort of fellows. A high-school English teacher, he lives in Silver Spring with his wife, poet Teri Ellen Cross Davis.

TERI ELLEN CROSS DAVIS is the author of a more perfect Union, 2019 winner of The Journal/Charles B. Wheeler Poetry Prize and Haint, winner of the 2017 Ohioana Book Award for Poetry. She's a Cave Canem fellow and the poetry coordinator for the Folger Shakespeare Library.

MARCY DILWORTH is a recovering finance professional finally immersing herself in writing. Her flash fiction and short stories have appeared in *FlashFlood Journal, Literary Mama, and Writer's Resist*. She lives in Northern Virginia with her family and their precocious rescue pup, Kirby. Find her on Twitter @MCDHoo41.

KAY WHITE DREW, aka Katherine White, M.D., is a retired physician who specialized in neonatology, the care of ill and premature newborns. Her essays have been published in *Grace in Darkness; Hektoen International, the Journal of Medical Humanities;* and the *Maryland Literary Review*. She lives in Rockville, MD, with her husband.

CORNELIUS EADY's seven poetry collections include: *Victims of the Latest Dance Craze*, winner of the 1985 Lamont Prize; *The Gathering of My Name*, nominated for a 1992 Pulitzer Prize; and *Hardheaded Weather* (Putnam, 2008). He is co-founder of the Cave Canem Foundation and a professor of English at SUNY Stony Brook Southampton.

DAVID EBENBACH is the author of eight books of poetry, fiction, and non-fiction, including the poetry collections *Some Unimaginable Animal* and *We Were the People Who Moved*. He lives in Washington, DC. You can find out more at davidebenbach.com.

LIZ EGAN teaches creative writing and directs the centers for writing and academic success at Millsaps College in Jackson, Mississippi. She holds an MFA from George Mason University. Her fiction has appeared in *SFWP Quarterly, MAYDAY Magazine, Parhelion*, and *ink&coda*, and was listed as a 2016 Gertrude Stein Award Finalist.

KRISTIN KOWALSKI FERRAGUT writes, teaches, plays guitar, hikes, supports her children in becoming who they are meant to be, and enjoys the vibrant writing community in the DMV. Her work has appeared in *Beltway Quarterly, Nightingale and Sparrow, Bourgeon, Mojave He[Art] Review, Anti-Heroin Chic*, and *Fledgling Rag* among others.

PETE FORTENBAUGH is 30 years old and from Maryland's Eastern Shore. He has been working on the fictional Chesapeake island of Johnsontown for nearly 10 years. His first book, a 91 page novella entitled *"Charles Thomas's Monday After Father's Day* or *Revelations: A Parable"*, is due to be published in early Spring 2021 through Head to Wind Publishing.

AMY FREEMAN divides her time between freelance writing and serving as Development Director for The Writer's Center in Bethesda, MD. Her work has been featured in *The Washington Post, Parents.com, HuffPost, Santa Fe Writer's Project, XRAY Literary Magazine, Gargoyle*, and the *Furious Gravity* anthology.

JESSICA GARRATT is originally from Sykesville, Maryland. Her book *Fire Pond* won the Agha Shahid Ali Prize for Poetry and was published by the University of Utah Press. She lives in University Park, MD, with her husband and daughter, and is pursuing a second career as a clinical psychologist.

ROBERT L. GIRON, author of five collections of poetry and editor of three anthologies, has poetry and fiction in national and international anthologies, among other publications. He currently is an associate editor for *Potomac Review* and is the editor-in-chief of ArLiJo and is the founder/publisher of Gival Press.

SID GOLD is the author of four full-length collections of poetry, including *Working Vocabulary* (WWPH, '97), and a two-time recipient of a Maryland State Arts Council (MSAC) Individual Artist Award for Poetry. Over forty years, his poems have appeared in numerous reviews and journals. A native New Yorker, he lives in Hyattsville, MD.

ARIEL M. GOLDENTHAL received her MFA from George Mason University where she is now an Assistant Professor of English. Her work has appeared in *Fiction Southeast, MoonPark Review*, and *Grace & Gravity Vol. VIII*.

CHRISTOPHER GOODRICH, a resident of Montgomery County, MD has published 3 books of poetry: *By Reaching* (Finishing Line Press), *Nevertheless, Hello* (Steel Toe Books) and *No Texting at the Dinner Table* (New York Quarterly Press). He is the recipient of an Emerging Writers Fellowship from The Writer's Center in Bethesda Maryland and two Dorothy Sargent Rosenberg Poetry Prizes.

CHRISTOPHER J. GREGGS is a poet, designer, and rap artist. He is a Cave Canem, Tin House, Callaloo, and Watering Hole fellow. His work has appeared in publications such as *TriQuarterly, Winter Tangerine*, and *Texas Review*, among others. His EP *Change Mah Name* is streaming on all platforms.

Kirsten Hampton's *The Ocean Cannot Be Blue*, was named in Beltway's 2019 Ten Best Books, as Cider Press Review Book Award finalist and Gold Winner Diversity Poetry Human Relations Indie Book. Hampton has received fellowships from *The Gettysburg Review*, Mid Atlantic Arts Foundation, and Virginia Center for the Creative Arts.

Melanie S. Hatter is an award-winning author of two novels and a short story collection. Selected by Edwidge Danticat, *Malawi's Sisters* won the inaugural Kimbilio National Fiction Prize, published by Four Way Books in 2019. *The Color of My Soul* won the 2011 Washington Writers' Publishing House Fiction Prize.

Shelby Settles Harper is a writer, art enthusiast, and sometimes-lawyer. She is a citizen of the Caddo Nation, an Indian tribe located in Oklahoma. Vices include Twitter, Tex Mex, and country music. Founder of Cahkeydonee Literary Project, this entity partners with tribes to put books and other reading materials in the hands of young people from reservation communities where public libraries are not readily accessible. Her published writing can be found at www.shelbysettlesharper.com.

Kathleen Hellen's collection *Umberto's Night* won the WWPH prize for poetry in 2012. Hellen's honors include prizes from the H.O.W. Journal, Washington Square Review, the Maryland State Arts Council and Baltimore Office of Promotion & the Arts. Her latest collection is *The Only Country Was the Color of My Ski*n.

Robert Herschbach is the author of a chapbook *A Lost Empire* (Ion Books, 1996) and a full-length book of poetry, *Loose Weather* (Washington Writers' Publishing House, 2013). He lives in Laurel, MD with his wife, two children, and two cats.

Amanda Hodes has an MA in Creative Writing from the University of East Anglia and is pursuing an MFA at Virginia Tech. Her poetry explores feminine performativity, the fashion-beauty complex, and structures of silencing. Her work has been recognized by the Arts Club of Washington, Sound Scene Festival, and elsewhere.

MATT HOHNER holds an MFA from Naropa University. An editor for Loch Raven Review, Hohner's first collection is *Thresholds and Other Poems* (Apprentice House 2018). His next collection is forthcoming from Salmon Poetry in 2022. He has published in *Prairie Schooner, Boyne Berries, Oberon*, and elsewhere. He lives in Baltimore.

EMILY HOLLAND is a lesbian writer with poems appearing in publications including *Nat. Brut, homology lit, bedfellows*, and *Wussy*. She is the author of the chapbook *Lineage* (dancing girl press 2019). Currently, she is the Managing Editor of *Poet Lore* and the Editor-in-Chief of *FOLIO* at American University.

DONALD ILLICH has published in various journals, including *Fourteen Hills, LIT*, and *Nimrod*. His full-length poetry collection is *Chance Bodies* (The Word Works, 2018). He lives in Maryland.

NATALIE E. ILLUM is a poet, disability activist and singer living in Washington DC. She is a three-time recipient of the DCCAH fellowship, and a 2019 Pushcart prize, Best of the Net, and Best New Poet nominee. She was a founding board member of mothertongue, a LGBTQA open mic that lasted 15 years. She has an MFA from American University. You can find her on Instagram and Twitter as @poetryrox, and as one half of All Her Muses.

REUBEN JACKSON is Archivist with the University of The District of Columbia's Felix E. Grant Jazz Archives. He is also an erstwhile radio host, a jazz critic, and the author of two volumes of poetry: *Fingering The Keys* (1990, Gut Punch Press) and *Scattered Clouds* (2019, Alan Squire Publishing)

GARINÈ ISASSI is a recovering journalist and the award–winning author of the humorous novel *Start with the Backbeat*. She lives in Maryland with her family, where she works in Marketing Communications, is the Workshops Chair for the Gaithersburg Book Festival and a Washington Writers Conference committee member.

NUBIA KAI is poet, playwright, and novelist who has been published in numerous anthologies and literary journals. She is a Larry Neal Writer's Competition winner and a recipient of two National Endowment for the Arts awards and six DC Commission on the Arts and Humanities awards for poetry.

Beth Kanter has written numerous essays and articles along with six non-fiction books including *No Access DC* and *Washington DC's Chef's Table*. Beth was awarded a 2019 James Kirkwood Literary Prize for her novel-in-progress, *Paved With Gold*, and first prize in the 2020 *Lilith Magazine* fiction contest. She helps others on their writing journeys through her coaching and non-fiction workshops.

Holly Karapetkova is the author of two books of poetry, *Words We Might One Day Say* and *Towline*. Her poetry, prose, and translations have appeared widely. She teaches at Marymount University and is currently serving as Poet Laureate of Arlington County.

Elizabeth Knapp is the author of *The Spite House* (C&R Press, 2011), winner of the 2010 De Novo Poetry Prize, and *Requiem with an Amulet in Its Beak* (Washington Writers' Publishing House, 2019), winner of the 2019 Jean Feldman Poetry Prize. An associate professor of English at Hood College, she lives in Frederick, Maryland.

Christopher Kondrich is the author of *Valuing* (University of Georgia Press, 2019), a winner of the National Poetry Series, and *Contrapuntal* (Free Verse Editions, 2013). New poems and essays appear *in The Believer, Bennington Review, The Kenyon Review*, and *Poetry Northwest*. An associate editor for *32 Poems*, he lives in Maryland.

Danuta E. Kosk-Kosicka is the author of two collections: *Face Half-Illuminated* (Apprentice House, 2015) and *Oblige the Light* (CityLit Press, 2015), winner of the fifth Clarinda Harriss Poetry Prize. Danuta is the translator for four books by Lidia Kosk. She is the Poetry Translations editor at *Loch Raven Review*. www.danutakk.wordpress.com

Len Kruger is a graduate of the MFA Program in Creative Writing at the University of Maryland. His short fiction has appeared in numerous publications including *Zoetrope All-Story, The Barcelona Review*, and *Gargoyle*. He recently retired from the Library of Congress and lives in Washington DC.

Mary Ann Larkin is the author of *That Deep and Steady Hum*, a book of poems published by Broadkill River Press, and of five chapbooks. Her work has appeared in numerous magazines and anthologies. She taught most recently at Howard University in Washington, DC. She divides her time between Washington and North Truro, Massachusetts.

KATEEMA LEE is a Washington DC native. Kateema is the author of two chapbooks, *Almost Invisible* and *Musings of a Netflix Binge Viewer*. Her forthcoming collection, *Transcript of the Unnamed*, explores joy, identity, violence, and the "brief, bright lives" of missing and forgotten black women in the District of Columbia.

NATHAN LESLIE won the 2019 Washington Writers' Publishing House prize for his collection of stories *Hurry Up and Relax*, his tenth book of fiction. He is currently the series editor for *Best Small Fictions*, he runs a reading series in Northern Virginia, and he is the publisher/editor of *Maryland Literary Review*. He has written for *The Washington Post, Kansas City Star, Orlando Sentinel, Orange County Weekly*, and many others.

STEVEN LEYVA was born in New Orleans, Louisiana and raised in Houston, Texas. He is a Cave Canem fellow and author of *The Understudy's Handbook*, which won the 2020 Jean Feldman Poetry Prize from Washington Writers Publishing House. Steven is an assistant professor at the University of Baltimore.

JONATHAN LEWIS is the author of *Babel On*, which won the 2017 L+S Press Mid-Atlantic Chapbook Series contest. His poetry has appeared in a variety of publications, including *Beltway Poetry Quarterly, Berkeley Poetry Review, Charleston Poets, Hawai'i Review, Northern Virginia Review*, and the *Washington Post*. Lewis lives in Washington, DC.

DAVID G. LOTT is poetry editor at *The Sligo Journal*, associate editor at *Potomac Review*, and author of the collection *New to Guayama*. His work has appeared in *Aethlon, Light, 100 Word Story*, and *Opium*, among other places.

GREGORY LUCE is the author of *Signs of Small Grace, Drinking Weather, Memory and Desire, Tile*, and *Riffs & Improvisations*. In addition to poetry, he writes a monthly column on the arts for *Scene4* magazine. He is retired from National Geographic, works as a volunteer writing tutor/mentor for 826DC, and lives in Arlington, VA.

MOHINI MALHOTRA is an international development economist and runs a social enterprise (www.artbywomen.gallery) to promote women artists and women's causes. Her fiction has appeared in *Gravel, West Texas Literary Review, Blink-Ink, Flash Frontier, 82 Star Review, A Quiet Courage, Writers' Center*. She's a DC citizen originally from Kathmandu.

CARON GARCIA MARTINEZ is a writer, teacher, and former diplomat who grew up in Los Angeles. A graduate of Williams College, the LSE (MS, Psychology) and George Mason University (MFA), Caron has taught at American University since 2008. Caron's published work is in short fiction and essays, and her current writing project is a novel set in Mexico in 1910, built on family stories recalled by her *abuela*, Celia.

OFELIA MONTELONGO, a Mexican bilingual writer, has published her work in *Latino Book Review*, *Los Acentos Review*, *Rio Grande Review*, and elsewhere. Ofelia was the 2019 Writer's Center Undiscovered Voices Fellow and the PEN America New Voices Fellow for the Emerging Writers Festival. She earned a MA in Latin American literature in 2020.

JENNY MOORE writes and edits fiction and nonfiction. Her writing has appeared in several anthologies, most recently *Furious Gravity*, the latest edition of the Grace and Gravity series. Jenny earned her MFA from the New School. She lives in northern Virginia and is currently finishing a novel. Learn more at jenny-moore.com.

SEAN MURPHY has appeared on NPR and been published in *USA Today*, *The New York Times*, *The Huffington Post, Salon, The Village Voice, The Good Men Project, Memoir Magazine*, and others. He has twice been nominated for the Push-cart Prize, and he is the Founding Director of 1455. Visit online at seanmurphy.net

JEAN NORDHAUS' 6 volumes of poetry include *Memos from the Broken World*, *My Life in Hiding, Innocence*, and *The Porcelain Apes of Moses Mendelssohn*. She has published work in *American Poetry Review, the New Republic, Poetry* and *Best American Poetry*.

GODDONNY NORMIL, born in New Jersey and reared in Port-au-Prince, works as a Senior Sales Manager with Jacobs Engineering Group where he's had the opportunity to work in the Middle East for several years. He now lives in Aldie, VA with his wife and two children.

MAURICIO NOVOA is from Glenmont, MD, the son of Salvadoran refugees. He received his MFA from Queens University of Charlotte and has had poems published in *Blue Mesa Review, Acentos Review, La Horchata Zine, Latino Book Review*, and the anthology *The Wandering Song: Central American Writing in the United States*.

KATHLEEN O'TOOLE, the current Poet Laureate of Takoma Park MD, has combined an active public life as a community organizer and trainer with writing and teaching. Her fifth and most recent collection of poetry, *This Far*, was released by Paraclete Press in 2019. Find her work at https://kathleenotoole-poetry.com.

ERIC PANKEY is a poet, essayist, and visual artist. He is the Heritage Chair in Writing at George Mason University.

LINDA PASTAN's 14th book of poems, *Insomnia*, was published in October of 2015 and won The Towson University Prize for Literature. She has twice been a finalist for the National Book Award, and in 2003 she won the Ruth Lilly Prize for lifetime achievement. *A Dog Runs Through It* was published in May of 2018.

PATRIC PEPPER has three chapbooks, and a full-length collection, *Temporary Apprehensions*, the 2004 winner of the Washington Writers' Publishing House Poetry Prize. His poetry and prose have appeared most recently, or are forthcoming, in *Barrellhouse, The Broadkill Review, Gargoyle, The Innisfree Poetry Journal*, and *The Sunlight Press*. Pepper lives in DC.

LESLIE PIETRZYK is the author of the novel *Silver Girl*. Her collection of stories, *This Angel on My Chest*, won the 2015 Drue Heinz Literature Prize. Short fiction/essays appear/are forthcoming in *Story, Southern Review, Ploughshares, Gettysburg Review, Hudson Review, The Sun*. She received a Pushcart Prize in 2020.

KIRSTEN PORTER is an editor, poet, professor, and guest lecturer. Her poems have been featured in *Poet Lore* and *The Limberlost Review*. Porter is the assistant to poet and literary activist E. Ethelbert Miller and the editor of *The Collected Poems of E. Ethelbert Miller*, published by Willow Books.

TAYLOR RAMAGE is the author of two poetry collections, *Forgive Us Our Trespasses* and *Lest I Know Your Weakness*. She is also a fantasy writer and has published other poems and short fiction in online magazines. Taylor loves stories in all forms and has something to learn from all of them.

COLLEEN KEARNEY RICH is the author of the chapbook *Things You Won't Tell Your Therapist* (Finishing Line Press, 2019) and a fiction editor at *Literary Mama*. Her writing has been published in *SmokeLong Quarterly, Wigleaf, matchbook*, and *Pithead Chapel*, among others. She lives in Virginia.

Kim Roberts is the author of *A Literary Guide to Washington, DC* (University of Virginia Press, 2018), and five books of poems, most recently *The Scientific Method* (WordTech Editions, 2017). She is the editor of *By Broad Potomac's Shore: Great Poems from the Early Days of Our Nation's Capital* (University of Virginia Press, 2020).

Patricia Schultheis is the author of *Baltimore's Lexington Market*, published by Arcadia Publishing in 2007, and of *St. Bart's Way*, an award-winning short story collection published by Washington Writers' Publishing House in 2015. Her memoir, *A Balanced Life*, was published by All Things That Matter Press in 2018. She is a member of the Authors' Guild and the National Book Critics Circle. More at www.pschultheis.net.

Adam Schwartz's debut collection of stories, *The Rest of the World*, won the Washington Writers' Publishing House 2020 prize for fiction. His stories have won prizes sponsored by *Poets & Writers*, *Philadelphia Stories*, and *Baltimore City Paper* and appeared in numerous literary journals. He has stories forthcoming in *Raritan* and *Gargoyle*. He has an MFA from Washington University in St. Louis. For twenty-three years, he has taught high school in Baltimore.

Leona Sevick is the 2017 Press 53 Poetry Award Winner for her first full-length book of poems, *Lion Brothers*. Her recent work appears in *Birmingham Poetry Review*, *Four Way Review*, and *The Rumpus*. She is provost at Bridgewater College in Virginia, where she teaches Asian American literature.

Courtney L. Sexton is the co-founder of the literary arts nonprofit, The Inner Loop. She is a DCCAH grant recipient, and a 2020 AAAS Mass Media Fellow. Her work has been featured in *The Fourth River, Sage, Smithsonian, District Fray* and elsewhere. She received her MFA from Sarah Lawrence College and is currently researching a dissertation on human-canine coevolution.

Gregg Shapiro lived in the Washington DC neighborhoods of AU Park and Capitol Hill (NE) from 1985-1988. The author of seven books, entertainment journalist/poet/fiction writer Shapiro now resides in Fort Lauderdale, Florida with his husband Rick and their dog Coco.

Kim Shegog is the 2019 recipient of the Judith Siegel Pearson Award for Fiction from Wayne State University. Her work has appeared in *The Sun, Appalachian Heritage, r.k.v.r.y quarterly*, and elsewhere. She holds an MFA from Converse College.

LAURA SHOVAN is an editor, educator, poet, and children's author. Some of her books include *Mountain, Log, Salt and Stone*, winner of the inaugural Harriss Poetry Prize; the anthology *Life in Me Like Grass on Fire: Love Poems*; and the children's novel-in-verse, *The Last Fifth Grade of Emerson Elementary*.

MYRA SKLAREW, professor emerita, American University, served as head of Yaddo Artist's Community and has published books of fiction, non-fiction and poetry, most recently, *A Survivor Named Trauma: Holocaust Memory in Lithuania*. She studied bacterial viruses and genetics with Max Delbruck and Salvador Luria at Cold Spring Harbor.

ROSE SOLARI is the author of three full-length collections of poetry, *The Last Girl, Orpheus in the Park*, and *Difficult Weather*; the one-act play, *Looking for Guenevere*; and a novel, *A Secret Woman*. Her work has appeared in many journals and anthologies. She is the co-founder of Alan Squire Publishing.

DANIELLE STONEHIRSCH works for First Book, getting diverse books to educators and kids around the country. Her short fiction, essays, and poetry have appeared in *Washington City Paper* and *Bethesda Magazine* as well as in anthologies *Roar: True Tales of Women Warriors* and *Reflections*, and on the *Tin House* website.

EVA K. SULLIVAN is a teacher at Richard Montgomery High School in Rockville, Maryland. She has been rowing and coaching in the DC area for more than 20 years. She hosts a writers' group with the Writer's Center of Bethesda and is a member of the Maryland Writers' Association. www.evaksullivan.com and Twitter @ergosullivan.

YERMIYAHU AHRON TAUB (www.yataub.net) is the author of six books of poetry and two books of fiction, including *Beloved Comrades: a Novel in Stories*. His most recent translation from the Yiddish is *May God Avenge Their Blood: A Holocaust Memoir Triptych* by Rachmil Bryks.

ADAM TAVEL's third poetry collection, *Catafalque*, won the Richard Wilbur Award (University of Evansville Press, 2018). You can find him online at www.adamtavel.com.

Washingtonian DARLENE TAYLOR is a lecturer and advocate for arts and literature. Her fiction and essays appear in anthologies and literary and historical journals. She holds an MFA from Stonecoast and fellowships from the DCCommission for the Arts and Humanities, American Association of University Women, Callaloo, and Kimbilio.

DAVID TAYLOR's collection, *Success: Stories*, received the WWPH fiction prize. His fiction has appeared in *Gargoyle, Potomac Review, Jabberwock, Washington City Paper*, and *Rio Grande Review*. His nonfiction includes *Cork Wars* and *Soul of a People*. David teaches with the Johns Hopkins Science Writing Program. He lives in DC.

VENUS THRASH is the author of the poetry collection, *The Fateful Apple*, which was nominated for the 2015 PEN Open Book Award. She has work forthcoming in *EMBODIED: A Feminist Graphic Poetry Anthology* and *The One Hundred Year House Poetry Anthology*.

CEDRIC TILLMAN holds a BA in English from UNC Charlotte and graduated from American University's Creative Writing MFA program. His debut collection, *Lilies in The Valley*, was published by Willow Books in 2013. His latest offering, In *My Feelins*, was published by WordTech in 2019. He currently lives in northern Virginia.

NICOLE TONG is the author of *How to Prove a Theory*, the 2017 Jean Feldman Poetry Prize winner and serves as the inaugural Fairfax Poet Laureate. Tong is the recipient of fellowships from Vermont Studio Center, Virginia Center for the Creative Arts, and George Mason University where she received an MFA.

ANDREW TRAN is a fiction writer from Virginia.

NORAH VAWTER earned her M.F.A. in creative writing from George Mason University. She's published in *The Washington Post, Memoir Magazine, The Nassau Review*, among others. "The Lucky Ones" is an excerpt of her autobiographically inspired novel, which she's currently querying. Norah lives in Northern Virginia with her husband and son.

An emerging Black poet, NABEELA WASHINGTON works towards her Masters in Creative Writing and English at Southern New Hampshire University. She was invited to read her poetry by the Takoma Park Poetry Reading Series and has been published in *Juke Joint Magazine*.

JACOB R. WEBER is a translator living in Maryland. He has published fiction in *New Letters*, (Robert Day Award for Fiction), *The Baltimore Review, Another Chicago Magazine, The Chattahoochee Review*, and other journals. His book of short stories, *Don't Wait to Be Called*, won the 2017 Washington Writers' Publishing House Award for Fiction.

KATHLEEN WHEATON's fiction has appeared in many journals and three anthologies, and she is a five-time recipient of Maryland State Arts Council grants. Her collection, *Aliens and Other Stories*, won the 2013 Washington Writers Publishing House Fiction Prize. Since 2014, she has served as president and managing editor of the Washington Writers' Publishing House.

ROBERT J. WILLIAMS is the author of the short story collection, *Strivers and Other Stories*. A resident of Washington, D.C., he is the recipient of four Larry Neal Writers' Awards given by the DC Commission on the Arts and Humanities. His work has also been published in Callaloo.

AHMAD WRIGHT is a DC based fiction writer. Credits include selections in *Connections Magazine* /The College of Southern Maryland, *African Voices Magazine*, and *Dark Dreams: A collection of Horror and Suspense by Black Writers*. He is currently an Assistant Professor at the University of the District of Columbia Community College.

MARY KAY ZURAVLEFF is the author of the novels *Man Alive!, The Bowl Is Already Broken*, and *The Frequency of Souls*. She is the founder of NoveltyDC and the winner of numerous fiction awards, including the American Academy of the Arts Rosenthal Award and DC Commission on the Arts Fellowships.

Post Script

The Washington Writers' Publishing House will resume our annual competition in 2021. Our award program is open to writers who live within 75 miles of our nation's capital. We will honor one poetry and one fiction manuscript with publication and a cash award of $1,000. The deadline is November 15. More details can be found on our website at www.washingtonwriters.org.

Read our award-winning poetry and fiction collections available via trade paperback and ebook everywhere fine books are sold.

Stay connected to WWPH:
on Facebook at the Washington Writers' Publishing House and
on Twitter @WWPHPress and Instagram @writingfromWWPH

CPSIA information can be obtained
at www.ICGtesting.com
Printed in the USA
LVHW030743210221
679521LV00002B/203

9 781941 551257